MEL BAY PRESENTS JUAN SERRANO

FLAMENCO GUITAR SOLOS

Juan Serrano uses and endorses LaBella strings.

A recording of the music in this book is now available. The publisher strongly recommends the use of this recording along with the text to insure accuracy of interpretation and ease in learning.

Visit us on the Web at http://www.melbay.com — E-mail us at email@melbay.com

CONTENTS

Special thanks to Leng Widjaja for his collaboration.

1st guitar
(solo)

ENSUEÑO
Petenera for Four Guitars

Juan Serrano

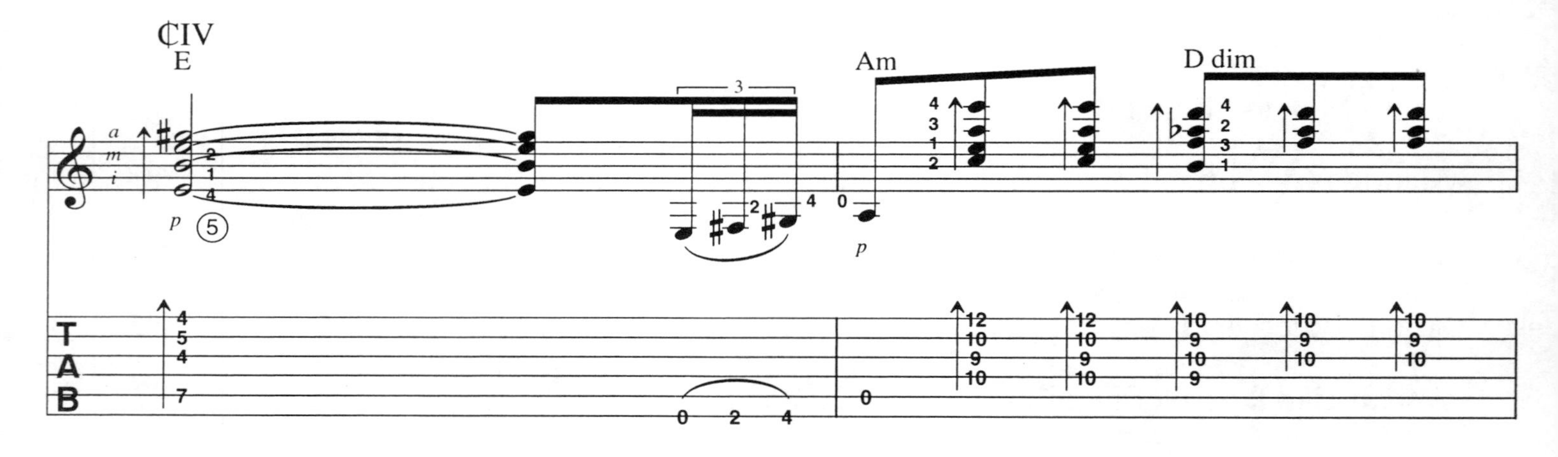

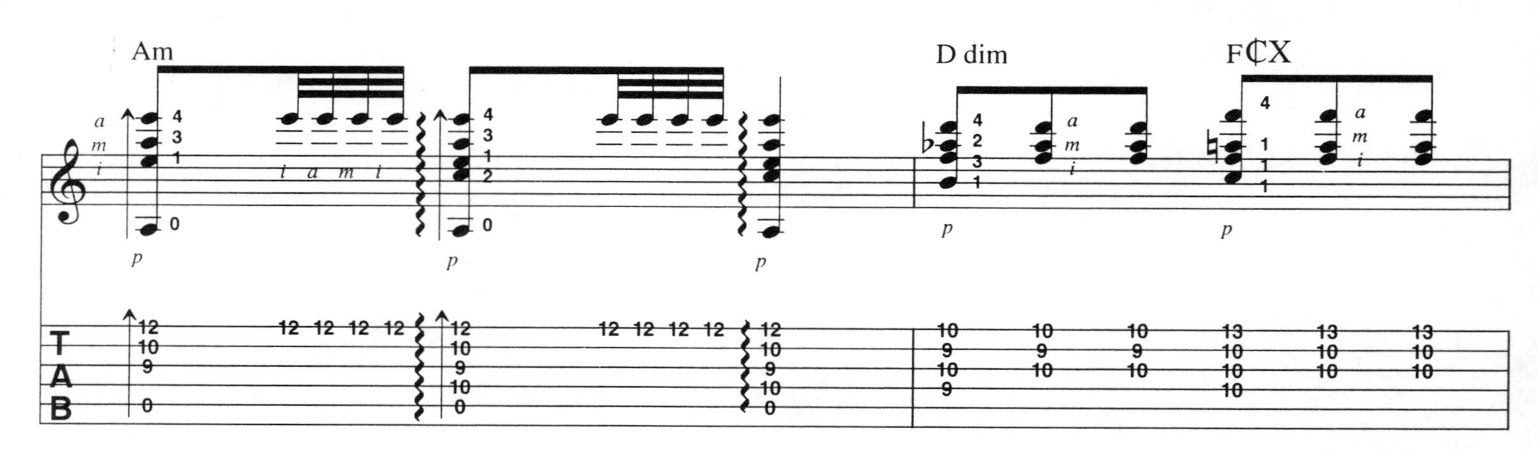

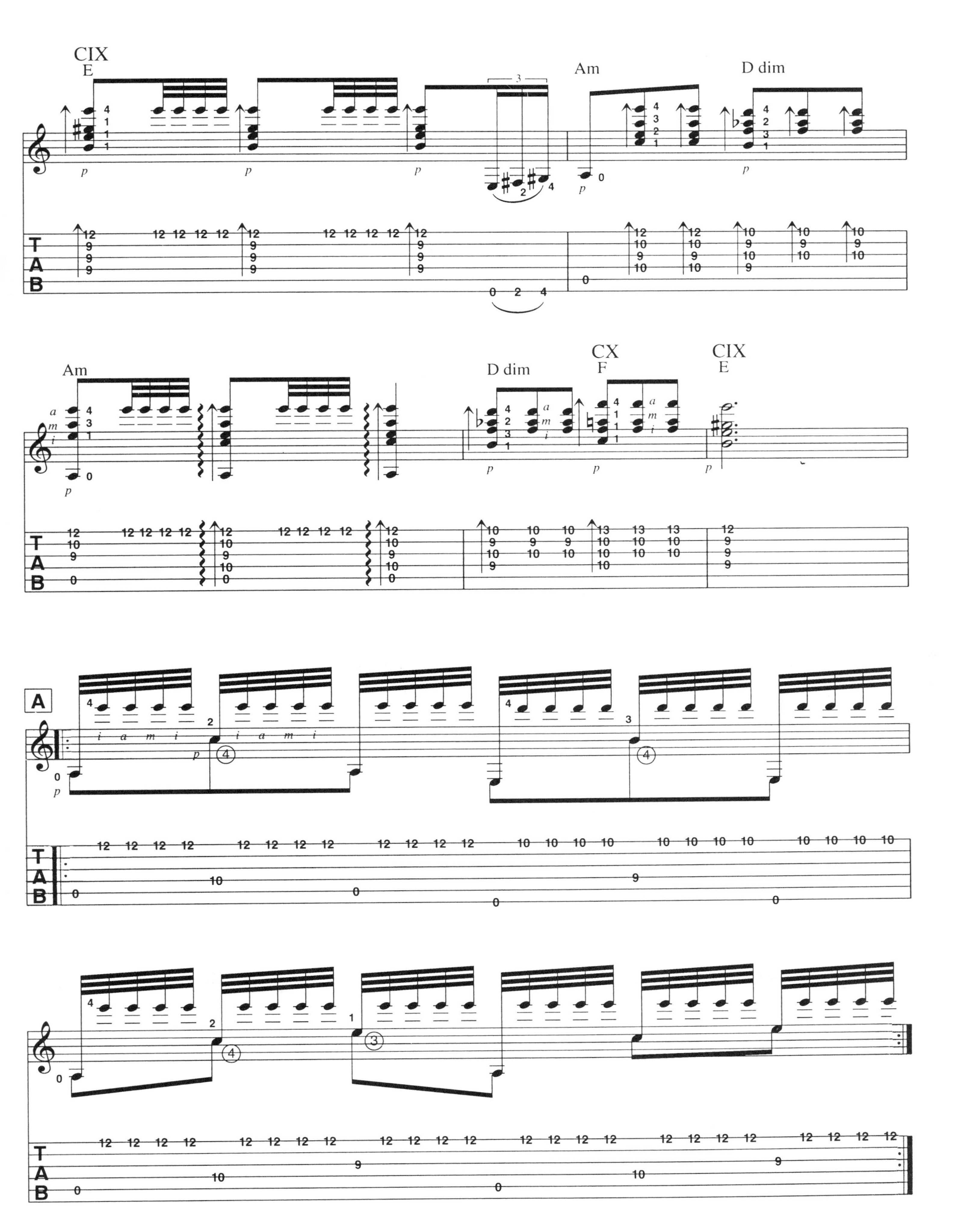
CIX
E
Am
D dim
Am
D dim
CX
F
CIX
E
A

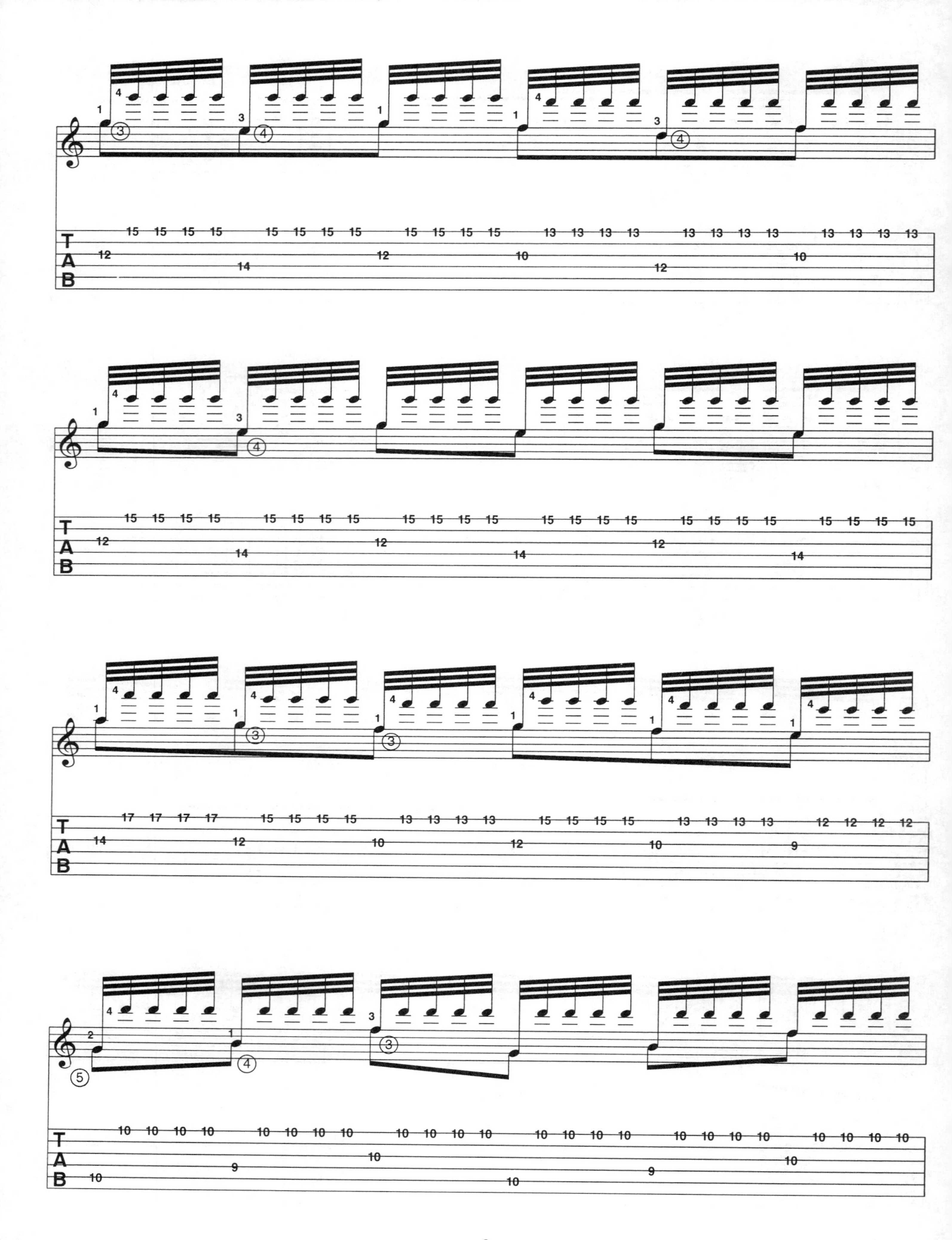

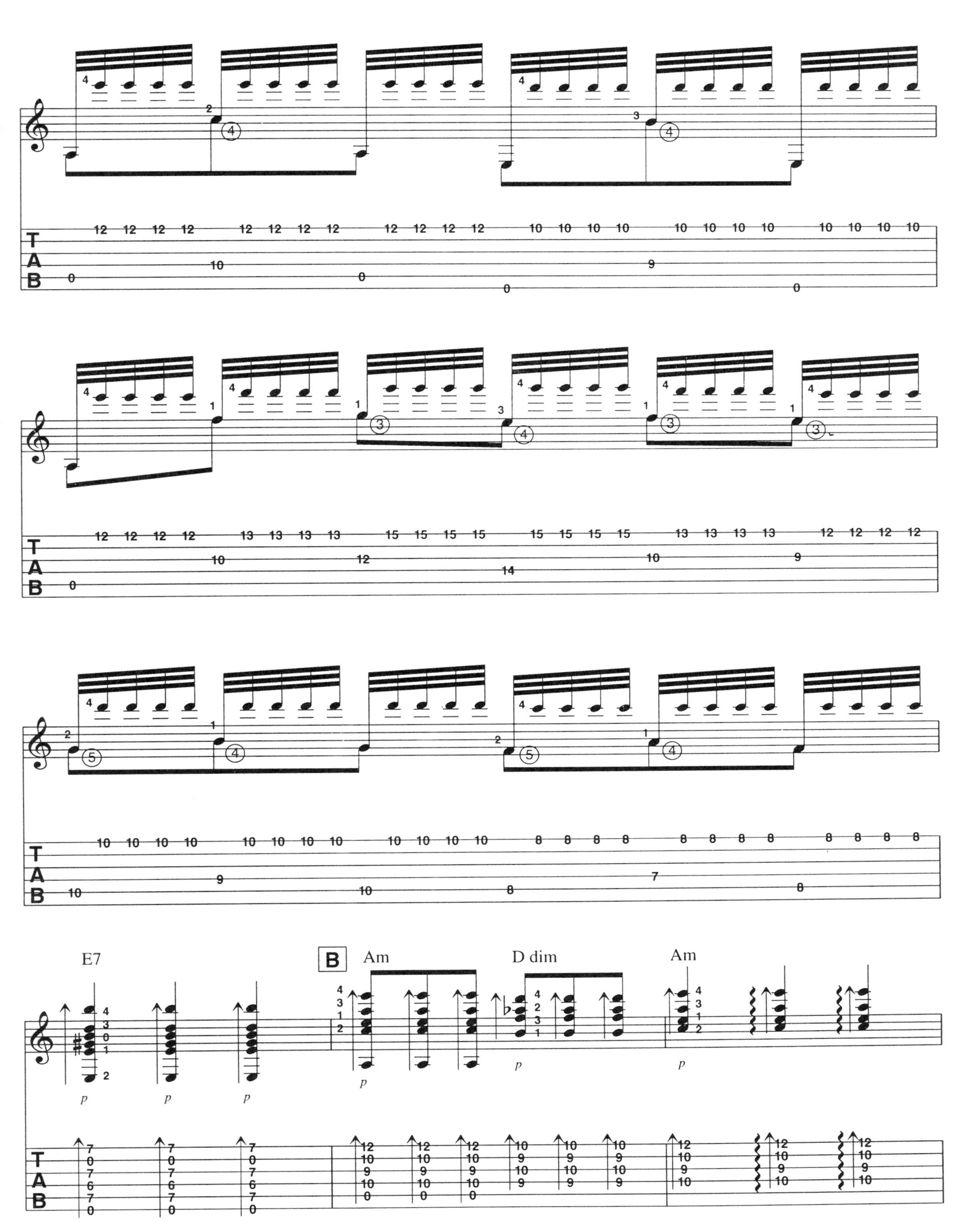
E7
B
Am
D dim
Am

D dim
CX
F
CIX
E
CV
Am
CIV
E
CV
Am
D dim
F7
E7
A dim
CVIII
C
CVII
E7

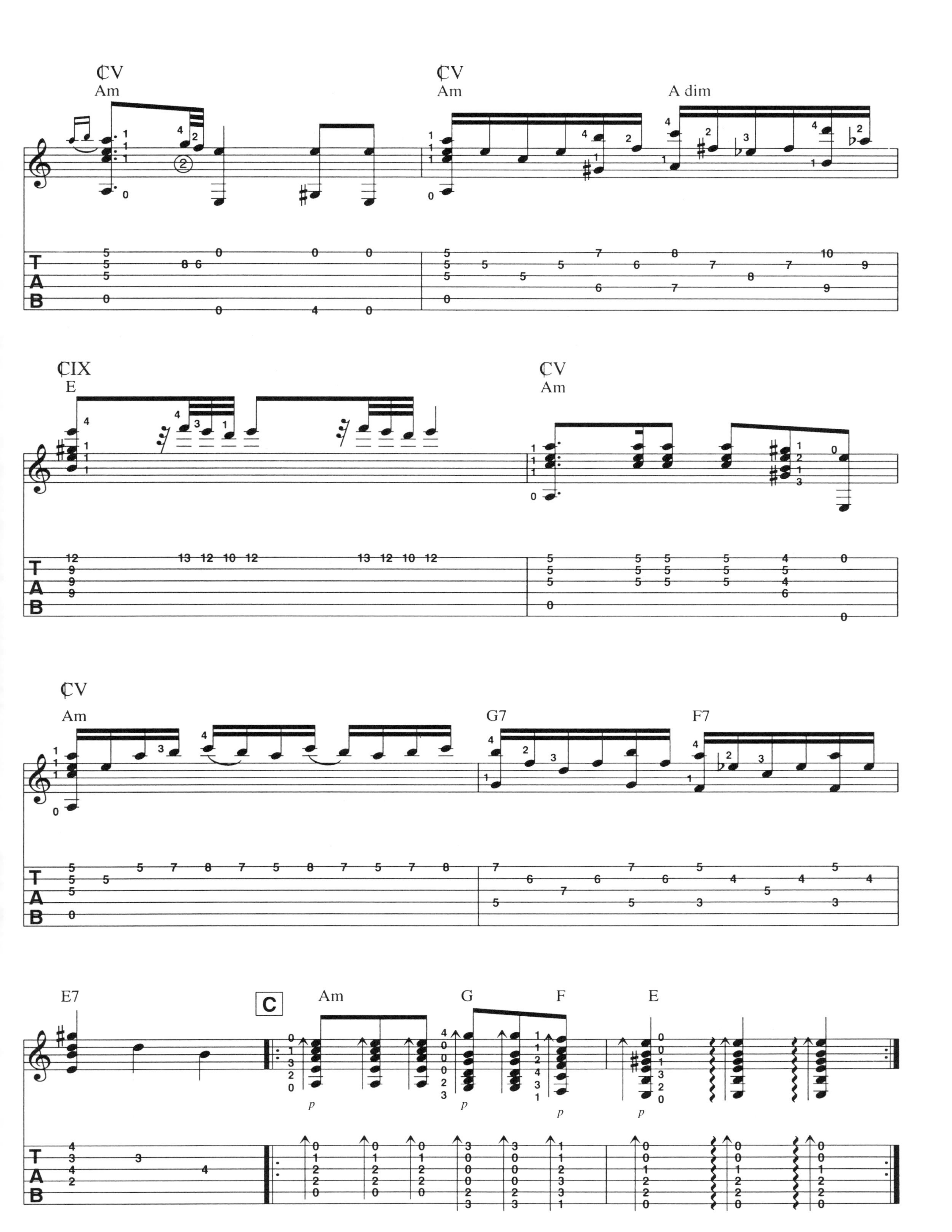
CV
Am
CV
Am
A dim
CIX
E
CV
Am
CV
Am
G7
F7
E7
C
Am
G
F
E

Am
E7
Am
G
F
E
Am
D dim
Am
Am
D dim
F7
CV
CVIII
CI
E

Am
E7
Am
G
F
E
G
F
E
ȻV
D

CX
CIX
F
E
CX
CIX
F
E
Am
E7
A
T
A
B

G
F
E
CIV
E
Am
E7

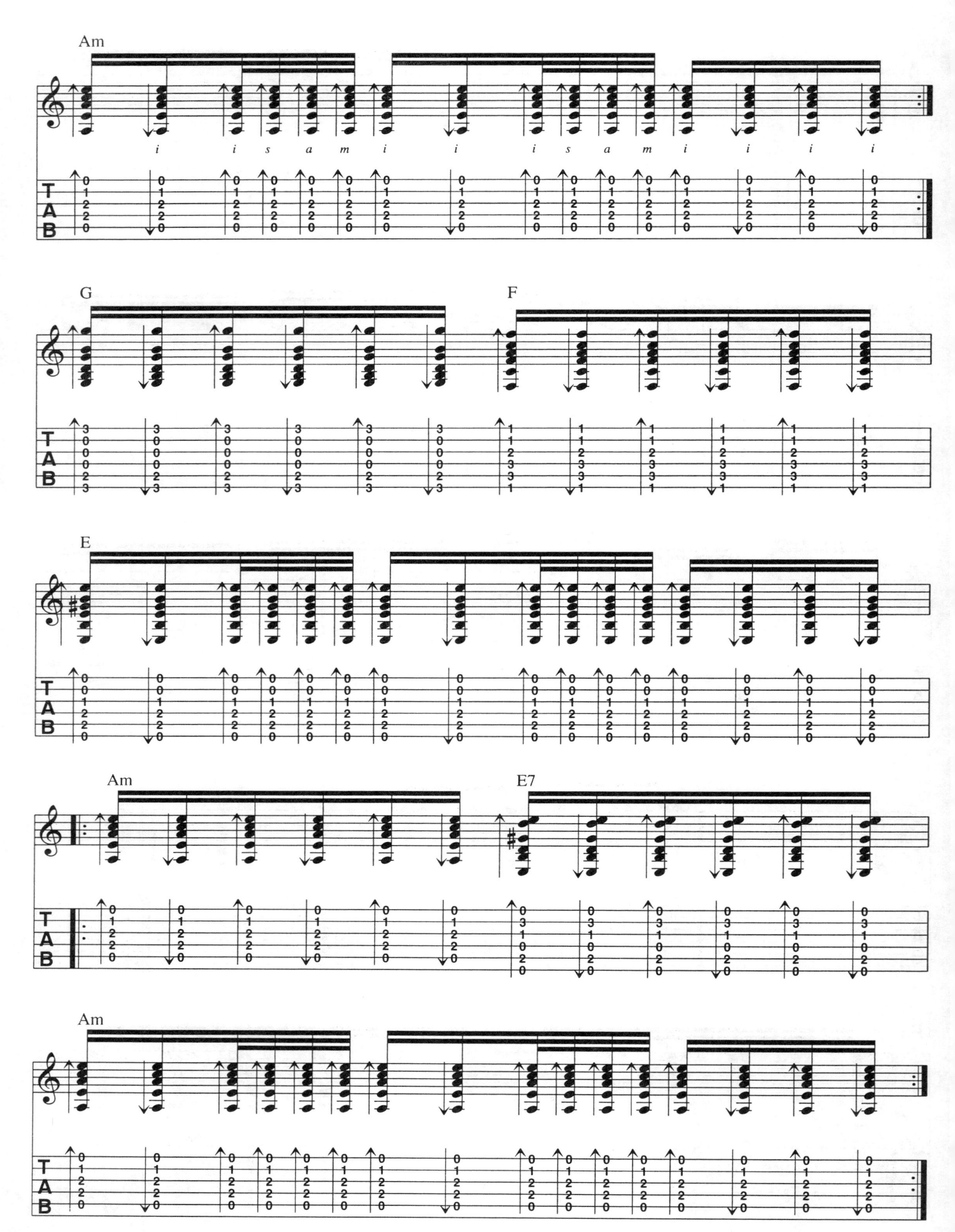
Am
i i s a m i i i s a m i i i i
G
F
E
Am
E7
Am

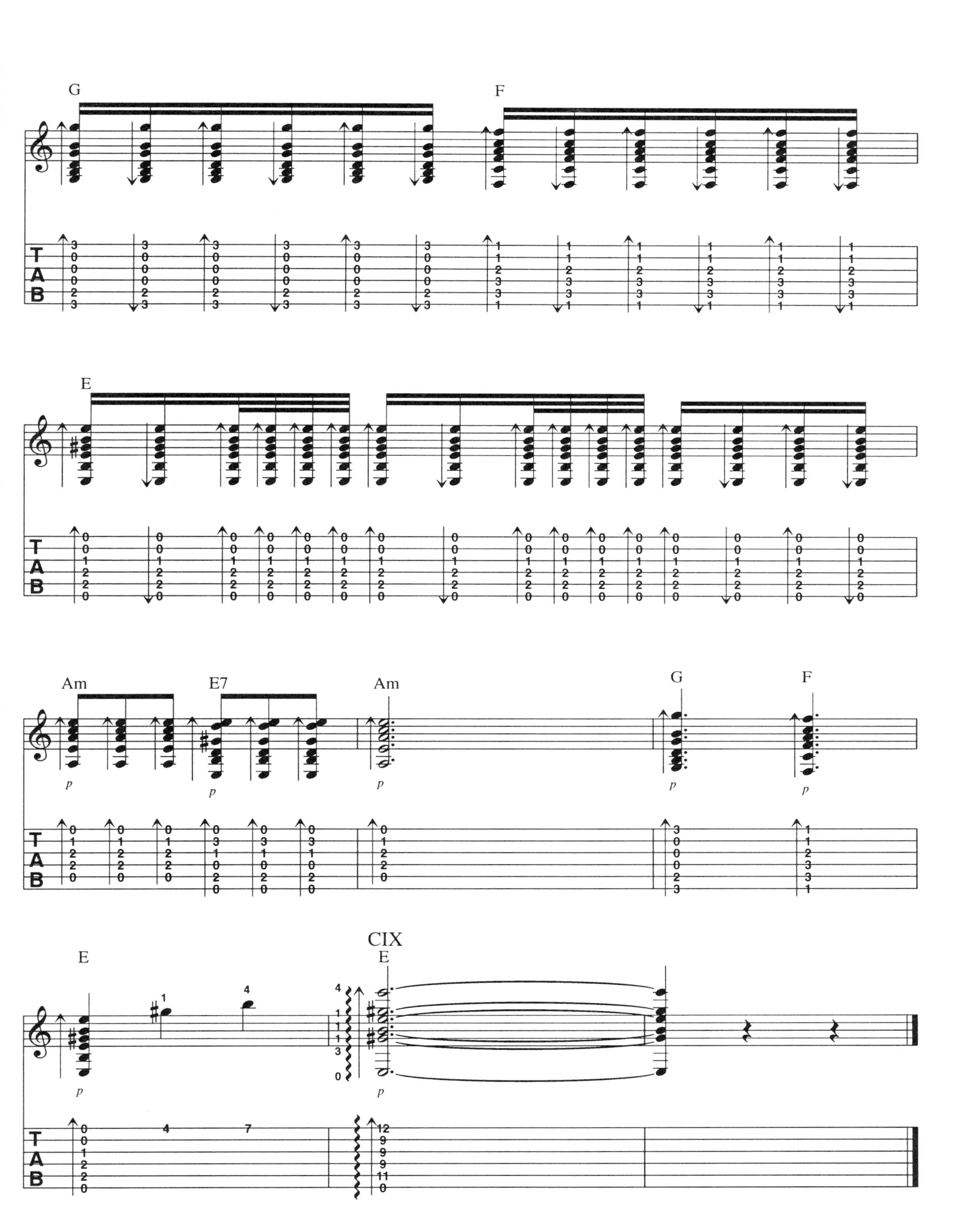
G
F
E
Am
E7
Am
G
F
E
CIX
E
p
TAB

Petenera

2nd guitar

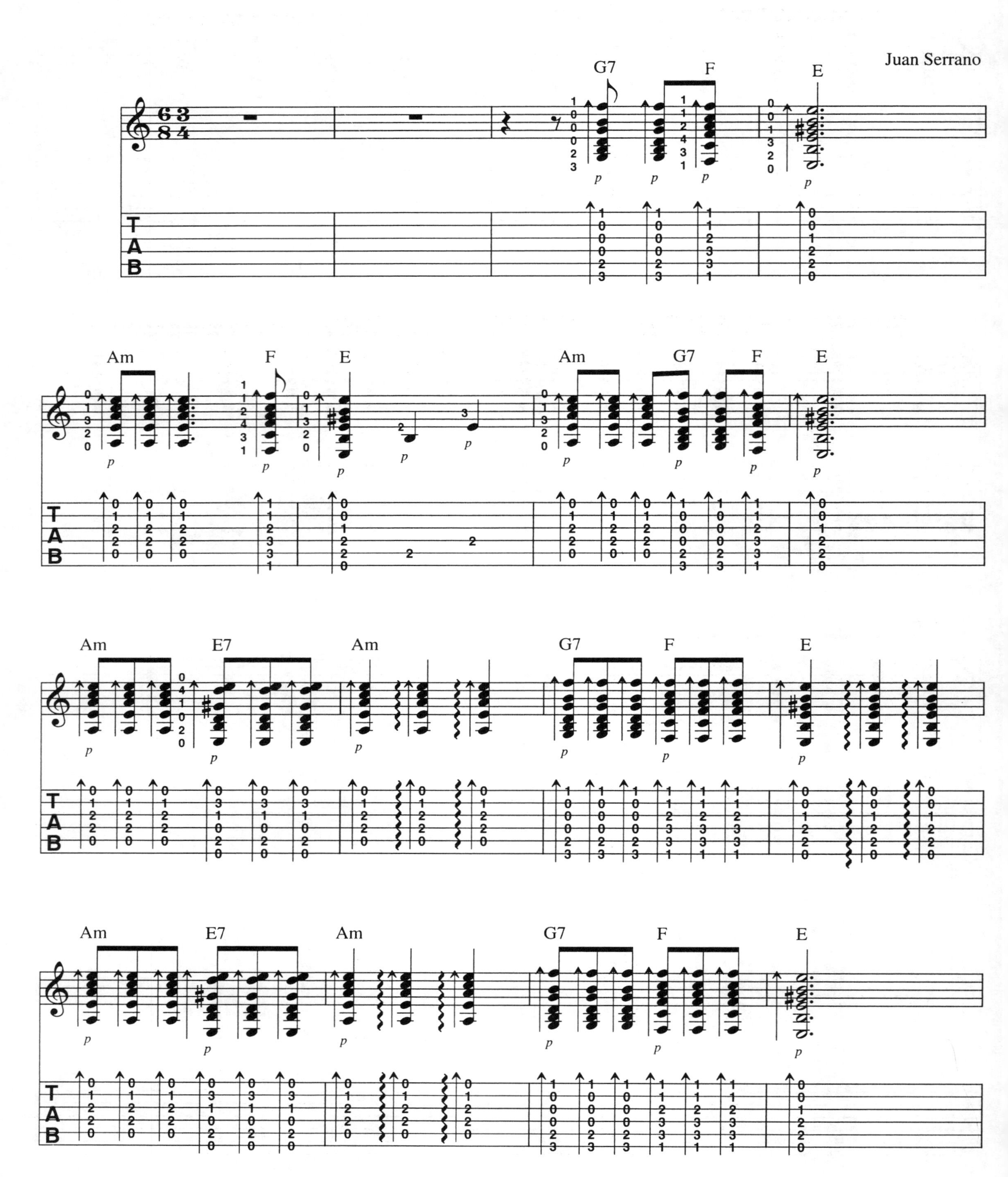

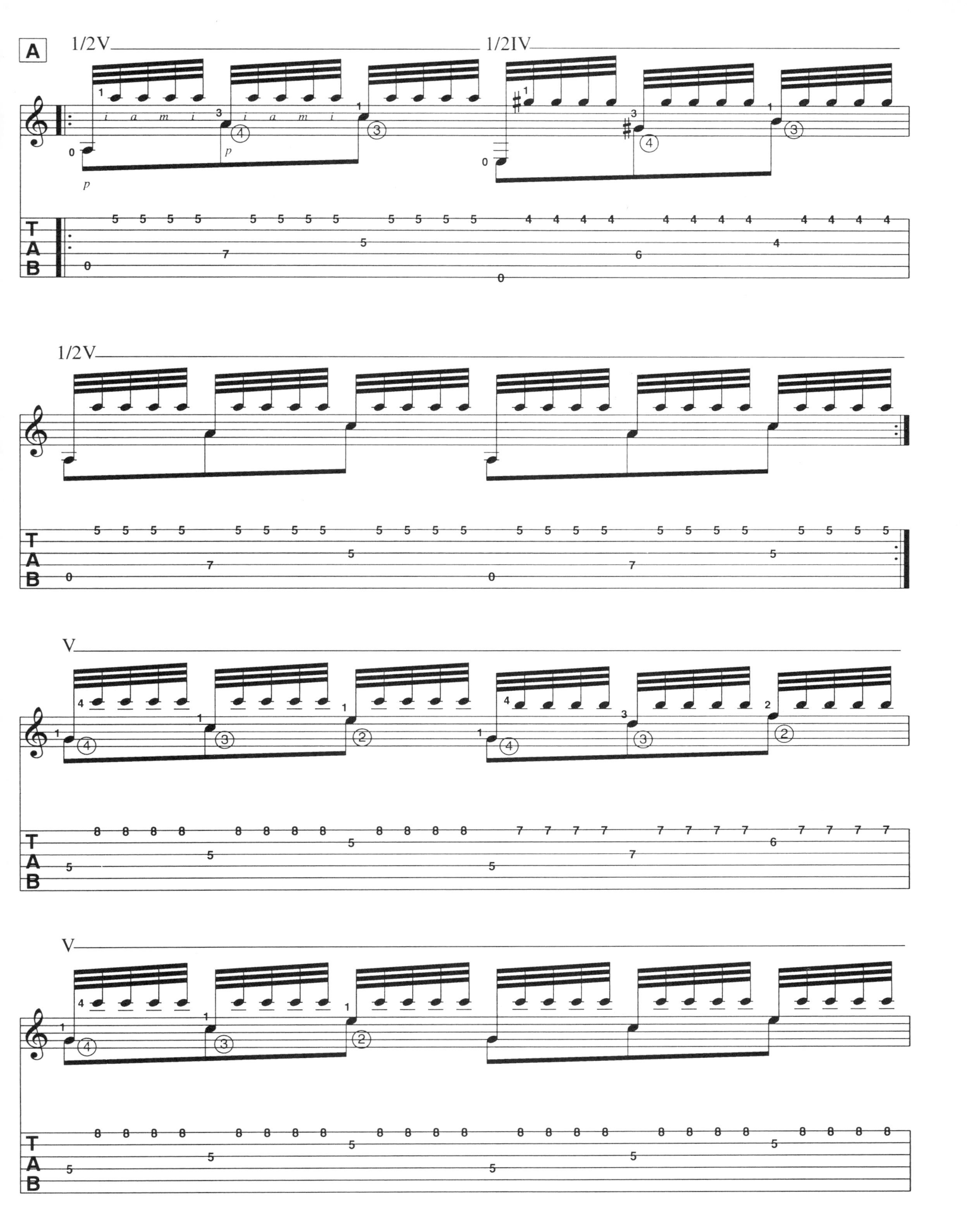
A
1/2V
1/2IV
i a m i
i a m i
p
p
1/2V
V
V
T
A
B

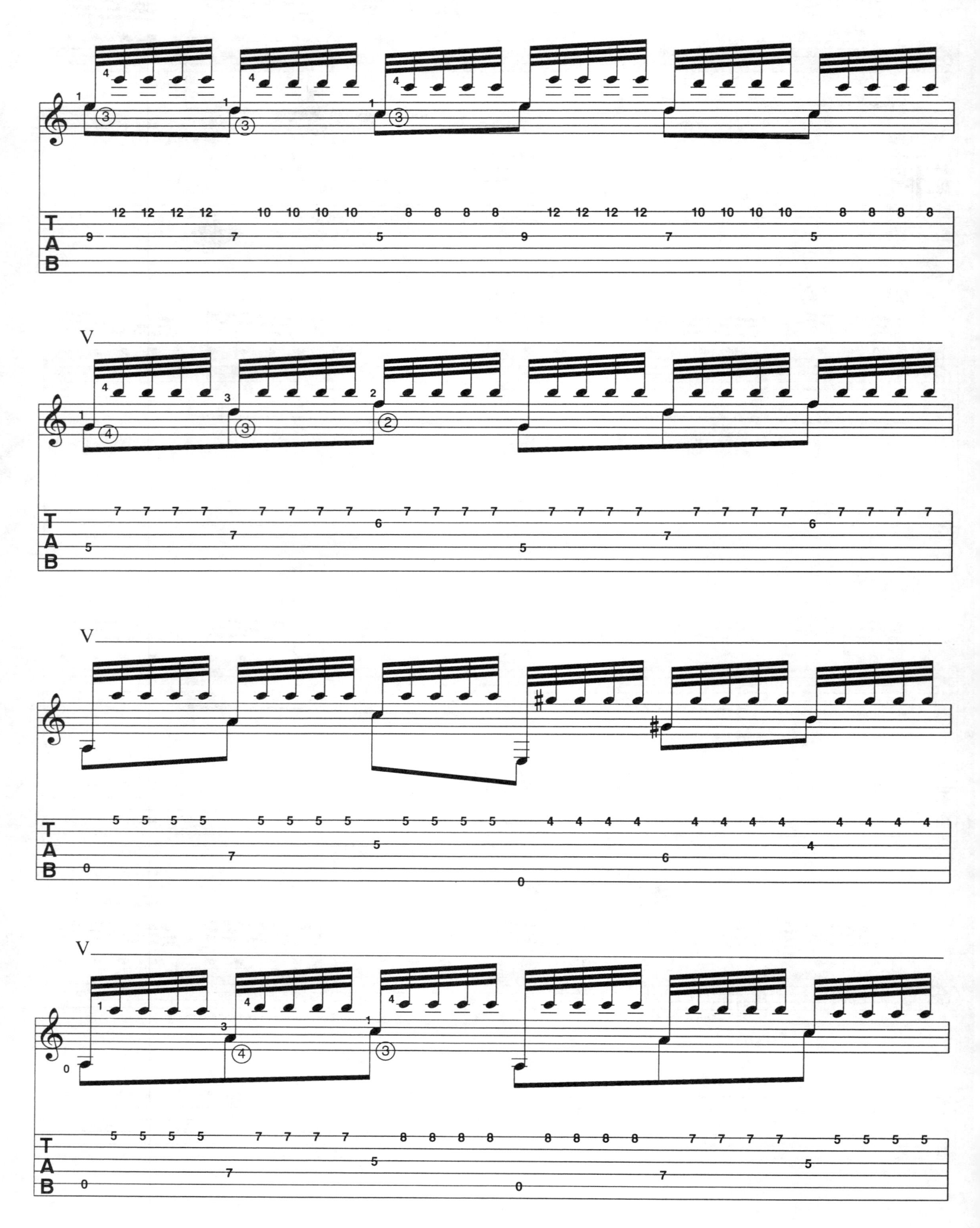

V
III
CII
E7
B
Am
E7
Am
G7
F
E
E

E
C
Am
G7
F
E
Am
E7
Am
G7
F
E
CV
Am
E
Am
C
G7
CV
Am
E
CV
Am
E
Am
E7
Am

G7
F
E
D

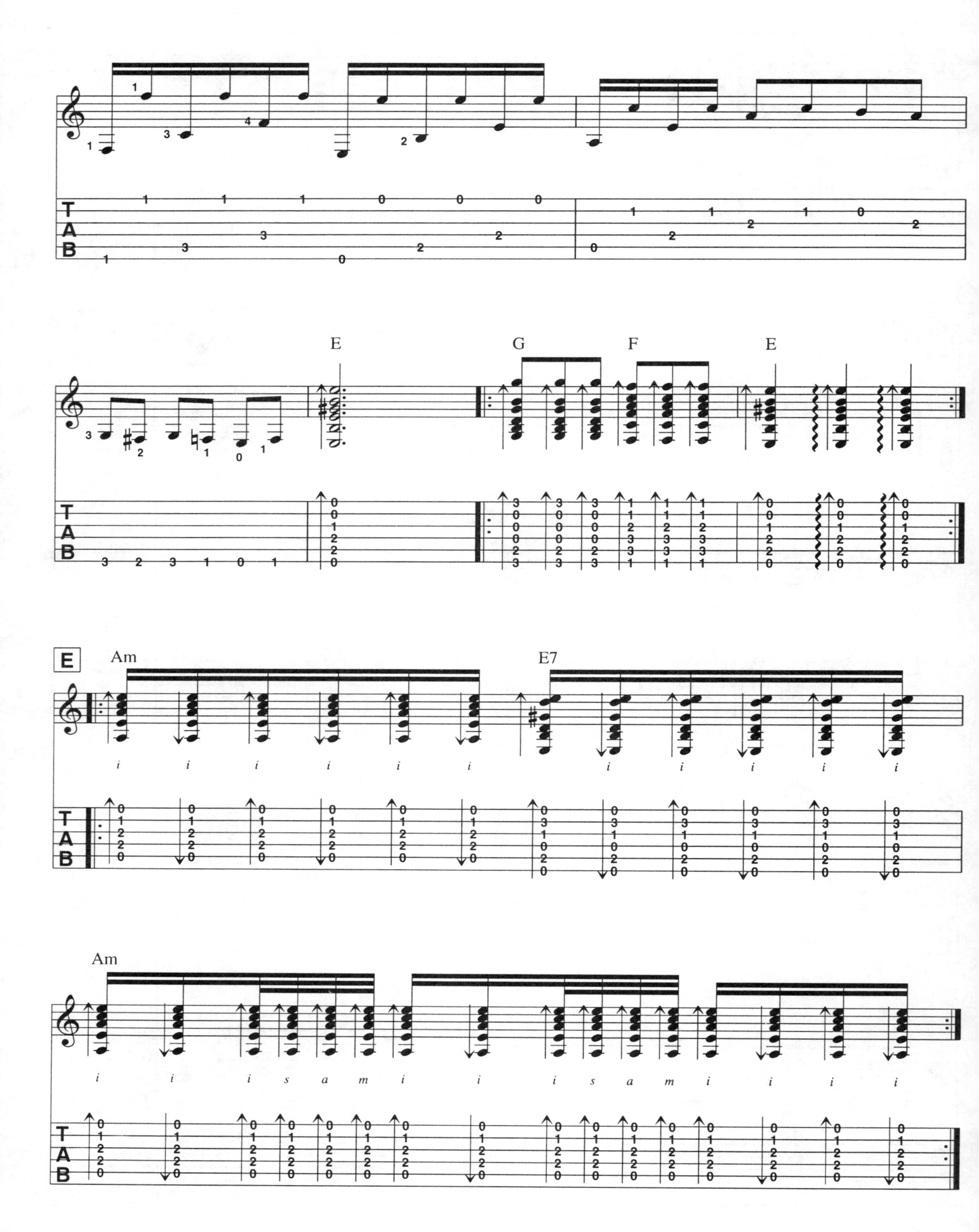
E
G
F
E
E
Am
E7
Am
i s a m

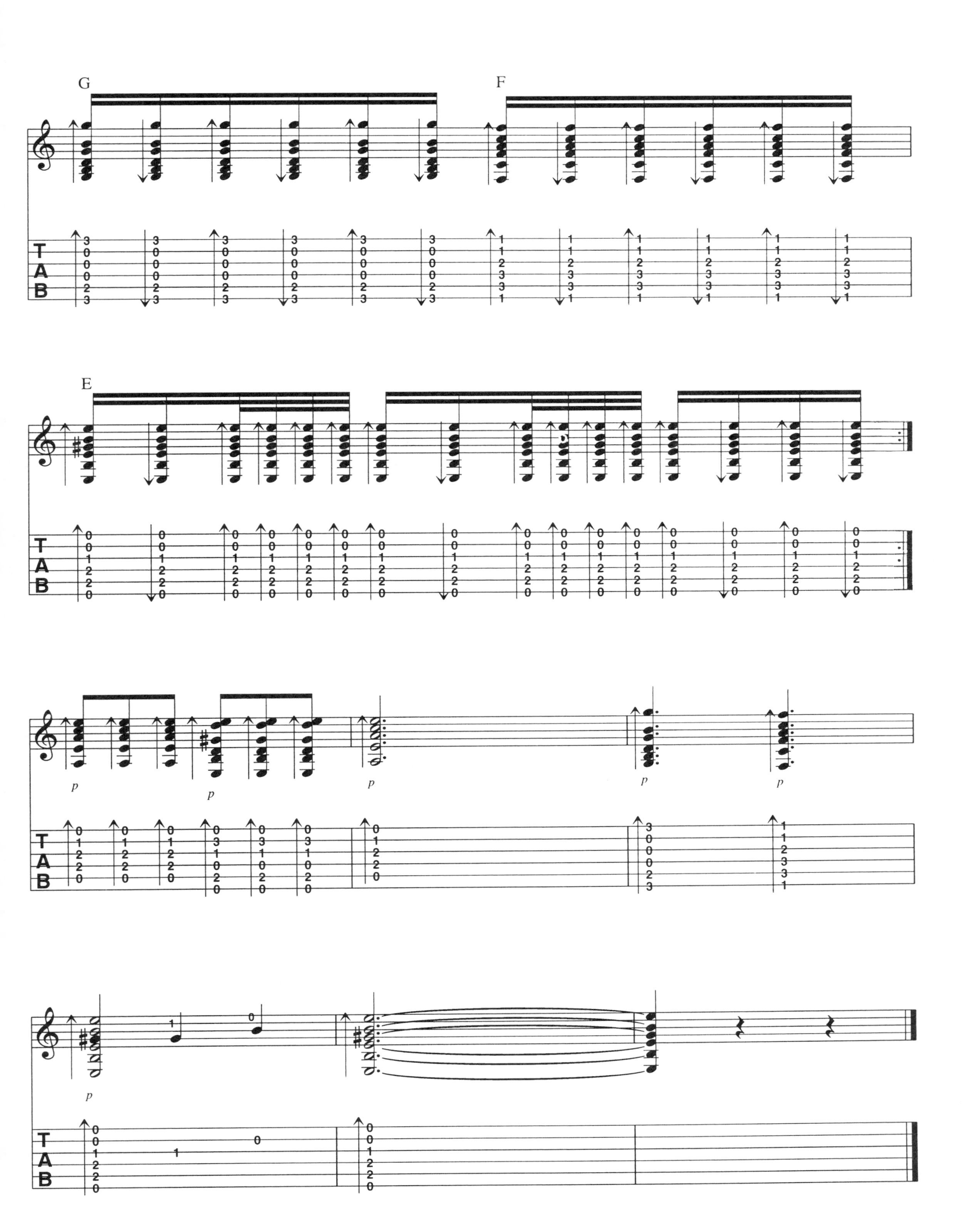
G
F
E
p
p
p
p
p
p
T
A
B

Petenera

3rd guitar

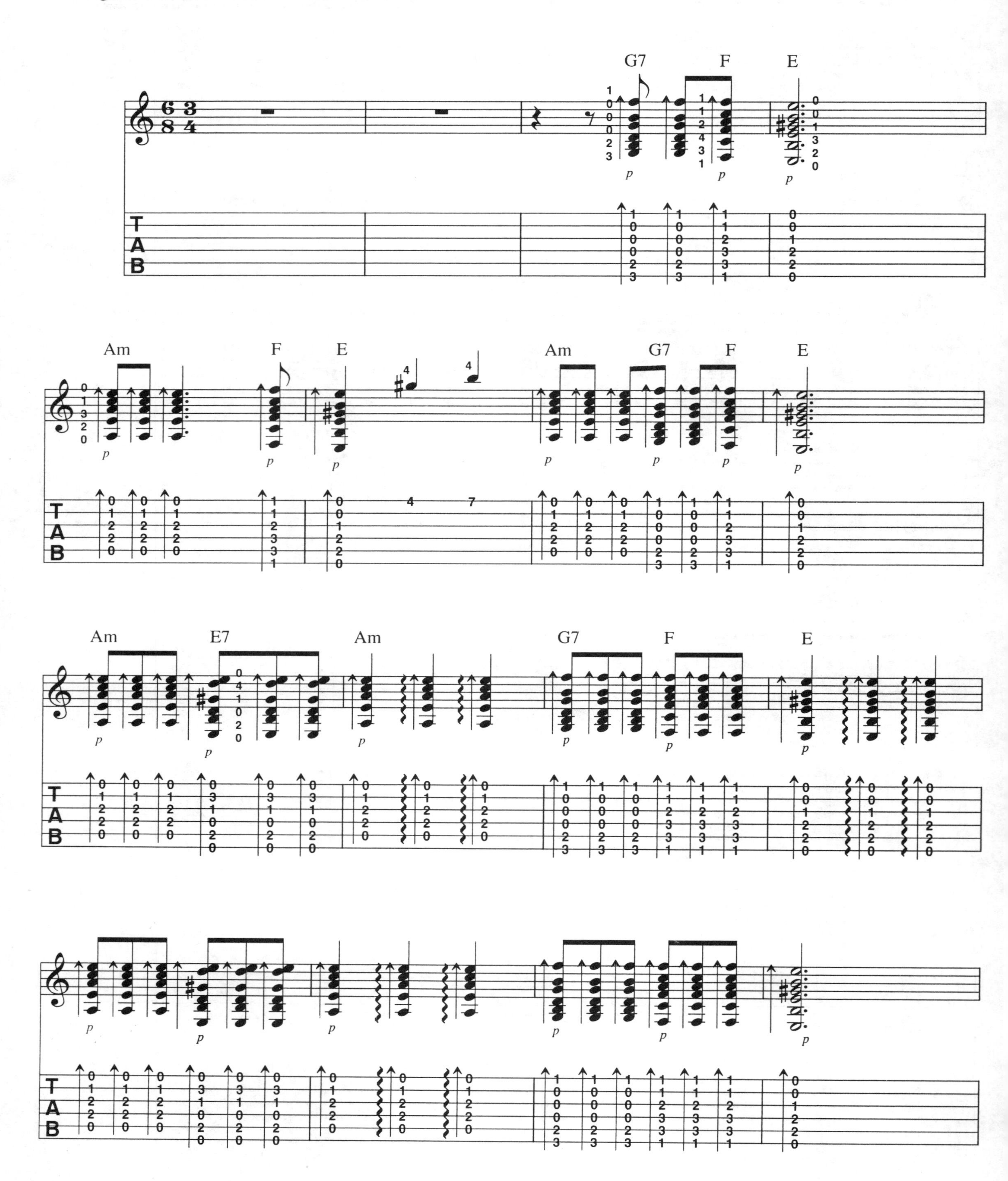

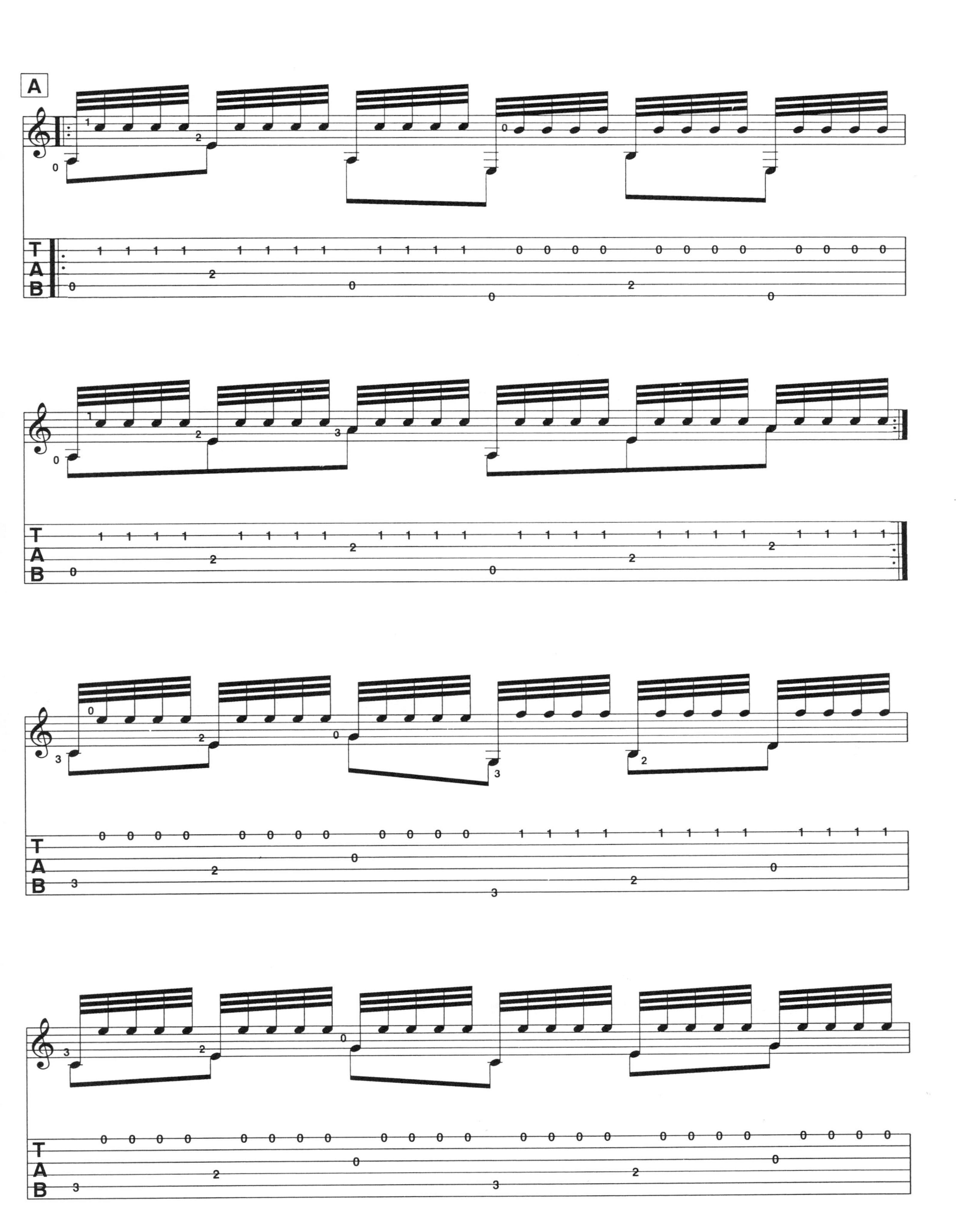
A

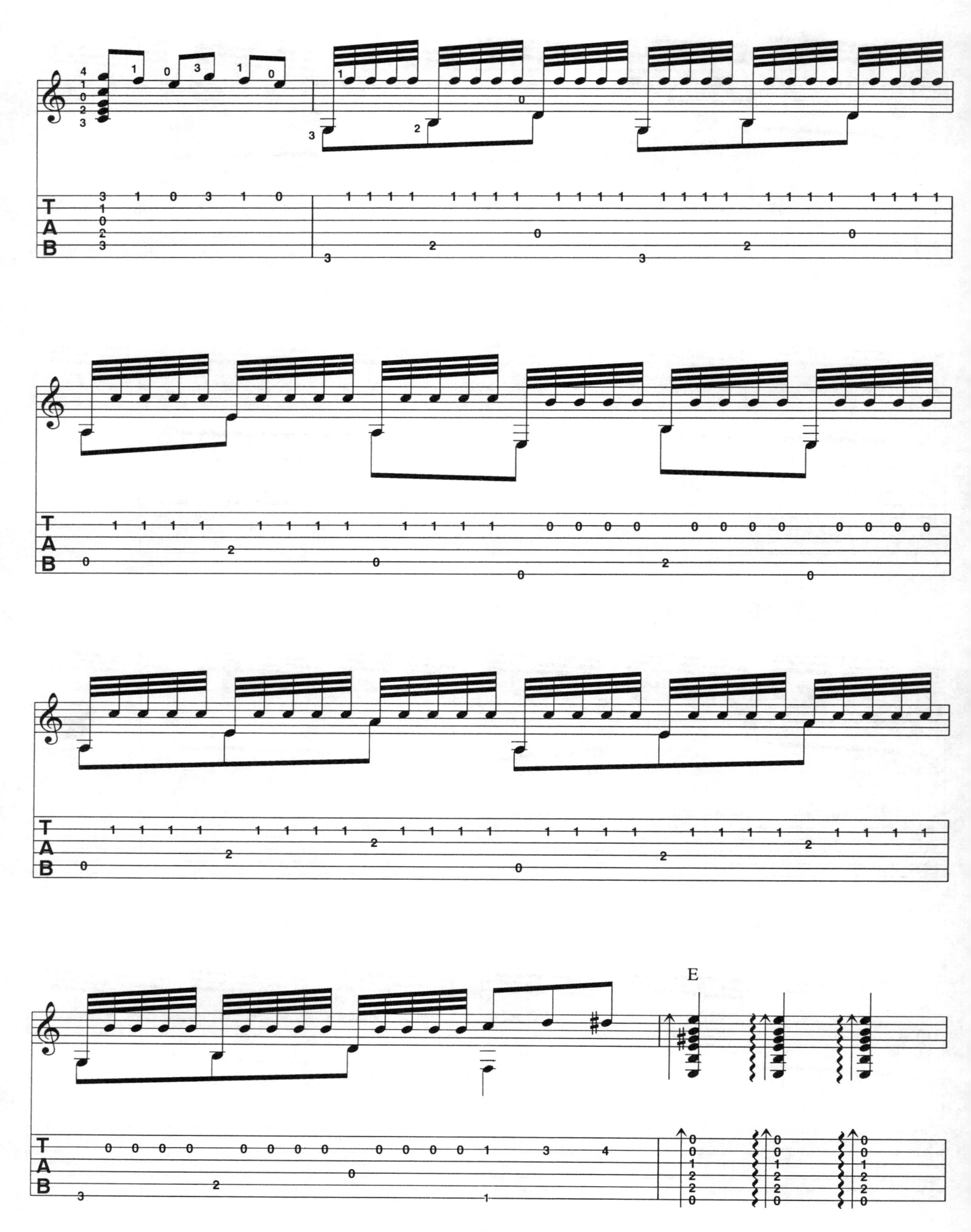
E

B
Am
E7
Am
G7
F
E

C
Am
E7
Am
G7
F
E
Am
E7
Am
T
A
B

G7
F
E
D
C
G7
F
E
Am
E7
Am
G7
F
E
E
E7
Am
CV
F
CIV
E
CV
Am
CV
G7
CIII
F7
CIII
E7
CVII
G
CV
F
CIV
E

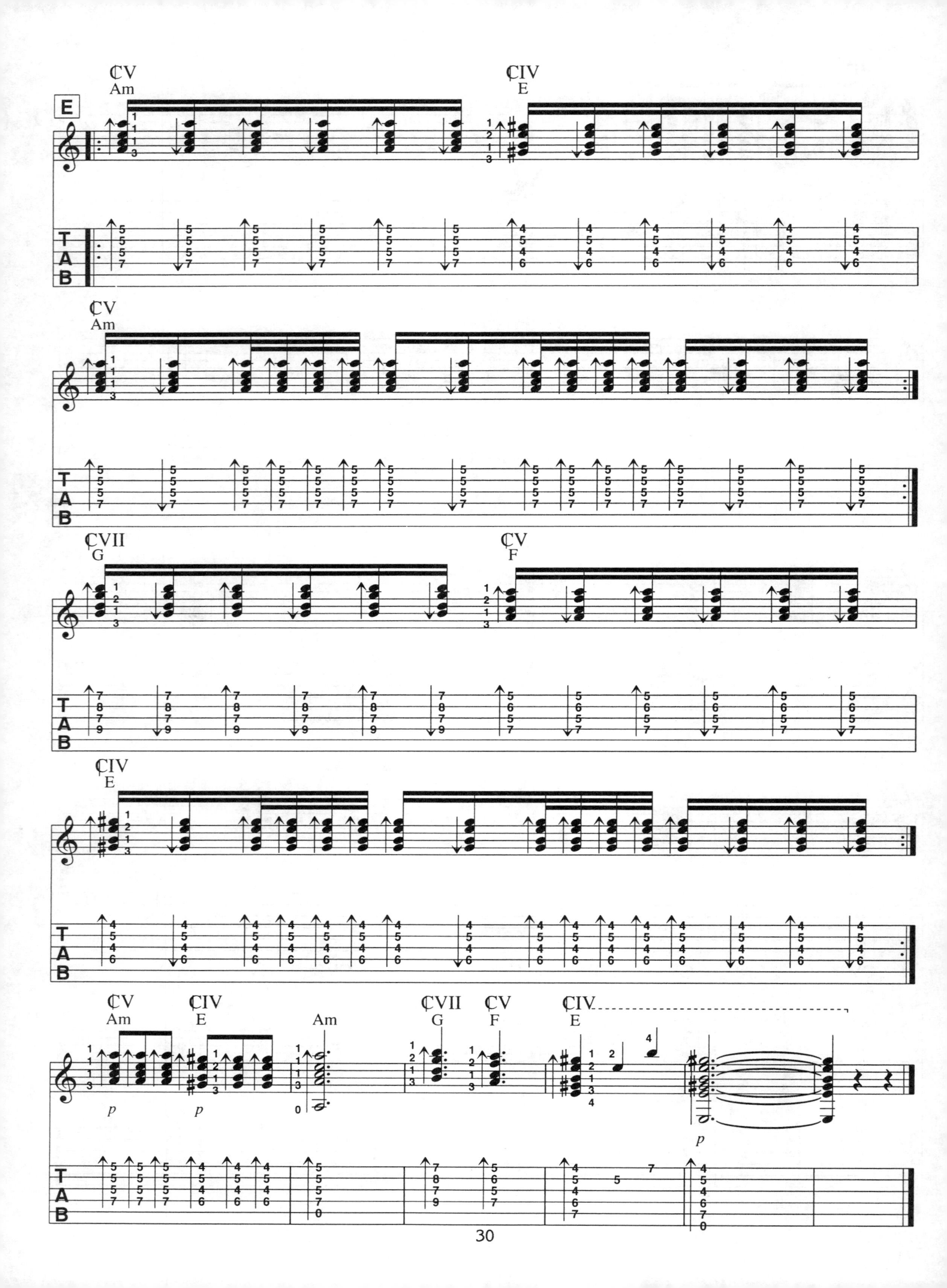
E
CV Am
CIV E
CV Am
CVII G
CV F
CIV E
CV Am
CIV E
Am
CVII G
CV F
CIV E
p
TAB

Petenera

4th guitar

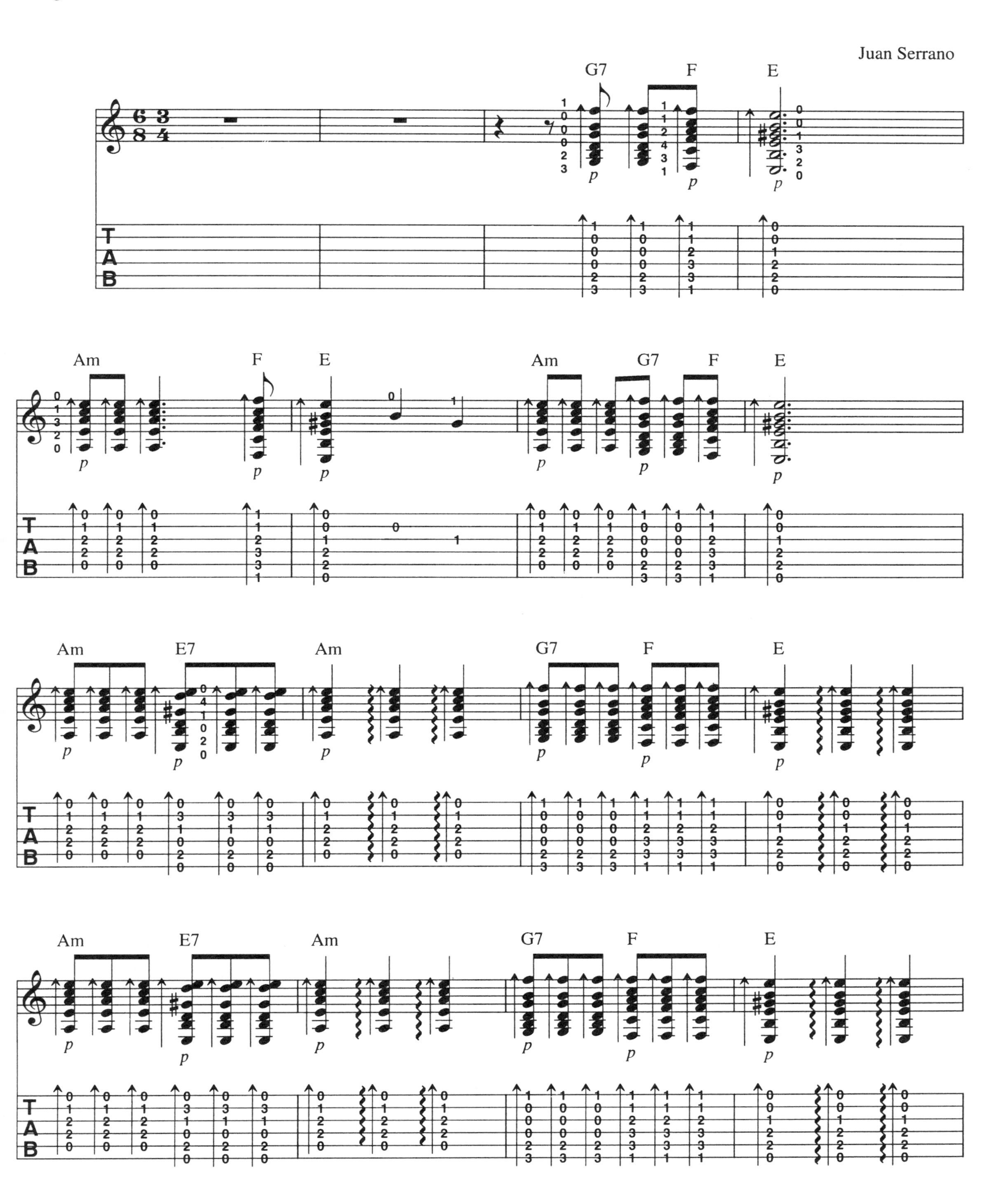

A
C
E
B
CV
Am
E7
CV
Am
CVII
G7
CV
F7
CIV
E7

C
Am
G7
F
E
Am
E7
Am
G7
F
E

Am
Am
E
Am
E7
Am
G7
F
E
G7
F
E
D

Am
E7
Am
G7
F
E
CIII
CV
CII
F7
G7
F7
E7
G
F
E

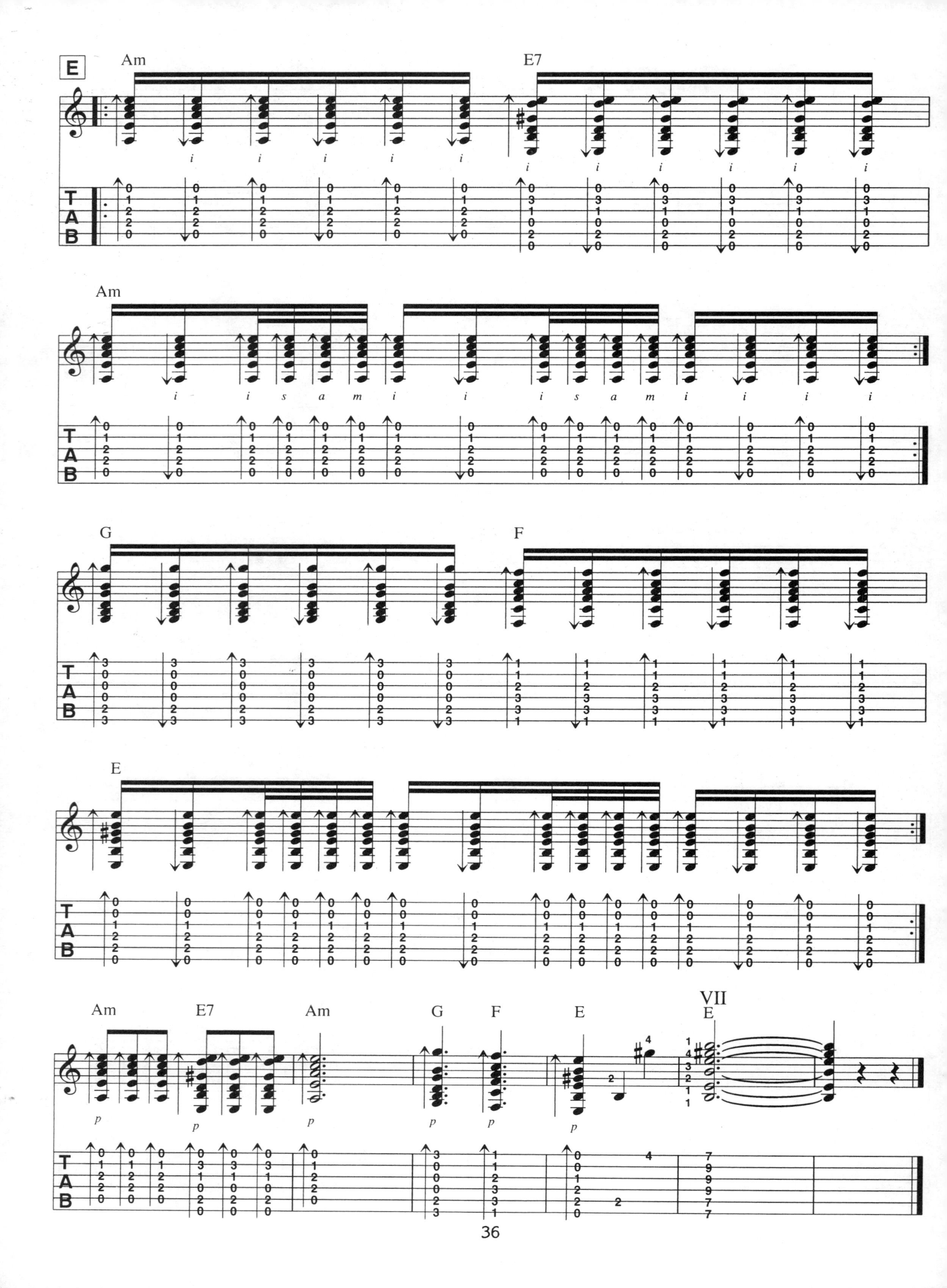
E
Am
E7
i i i i i i i i i i i
TAB
Am
i i s a m i i i s a m i i i i
G
F
E
Am E7 Am G F E
p p p p p p
VII
E

FLAMENCO DANCE
Sevillanas for Four Guitars
Sevillanas I

Guitar 1

Juan Serrano

Sevillanas II

Guitar 1

Juan Serrano

Sevillanas III

Guitar 1

Juan Serrano

Sevillanas IV

Sevillanas I

Sevillanas II

Guitar 2

Juan Serrano

Sevillanas III

Guitar 2

Juan Serrano

Sevillanas IV

Guitar 2

Juan Serrano

Sevillanas I

Guitar 3

Juan Serrano

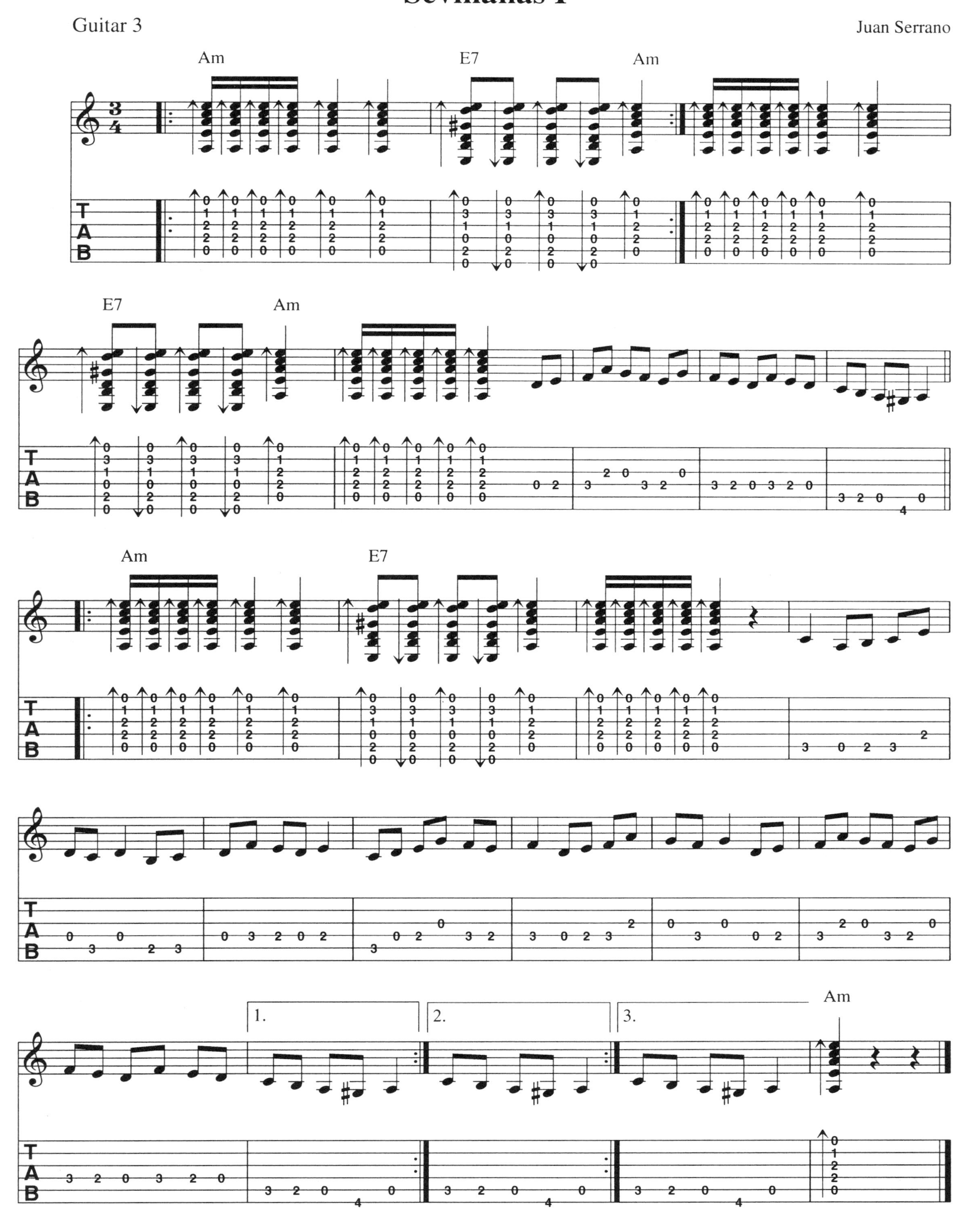

Sevillanas II

Sevillanas III

Guitar 3

Juan Serrano

Sevillanas IV

Guitar 3

Juan Serrano

Sevillanas I

Guitar 4

Juan Serrano

Intro

Am E7 Am

E7 Am

Salida

Am E7 Am

Copla

Sevillanas II

Guitar 4

Juan Serrano

Sevillanas III

Sevillanas IV

CANTO MINERO
Taranto

Juan Serrano

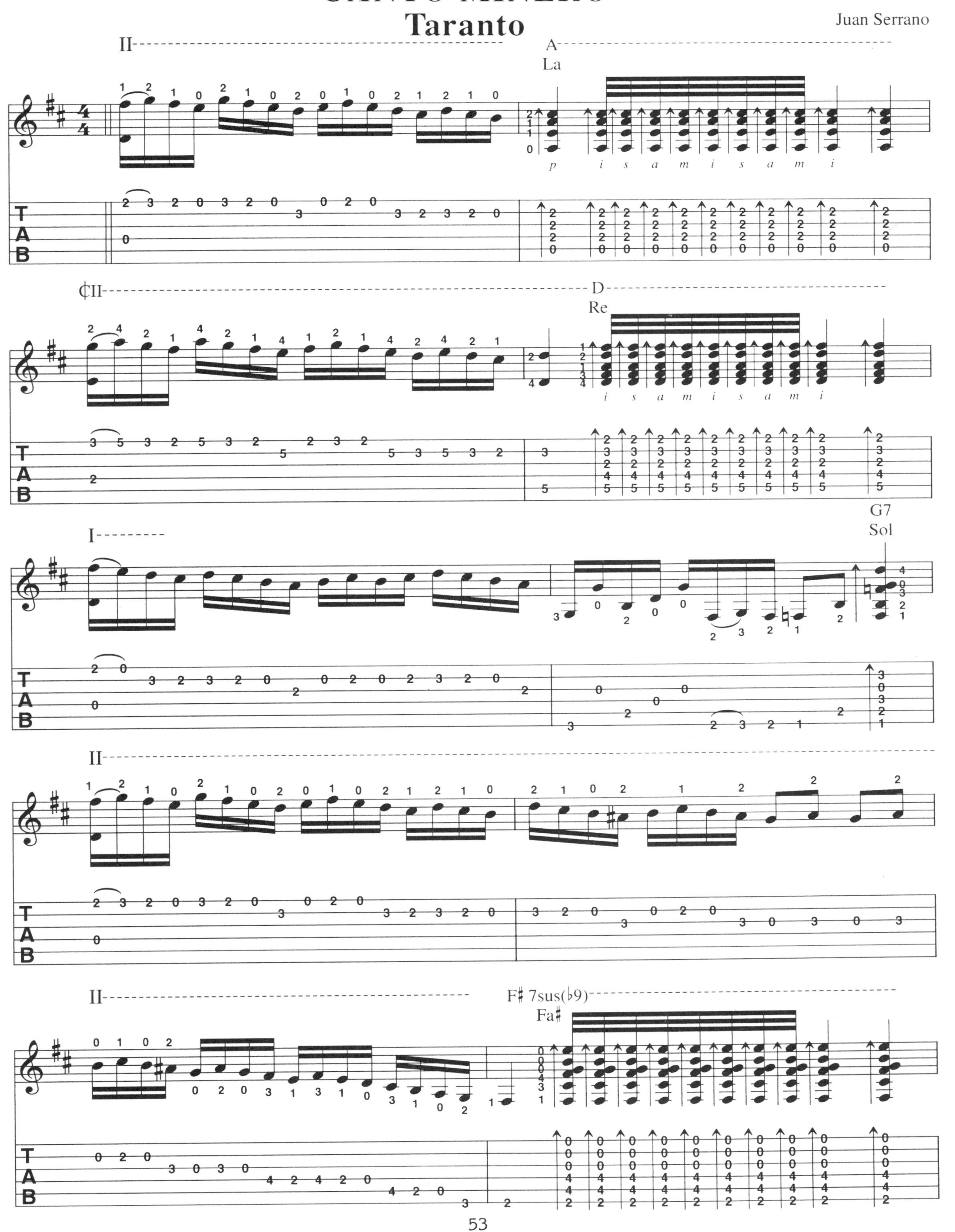

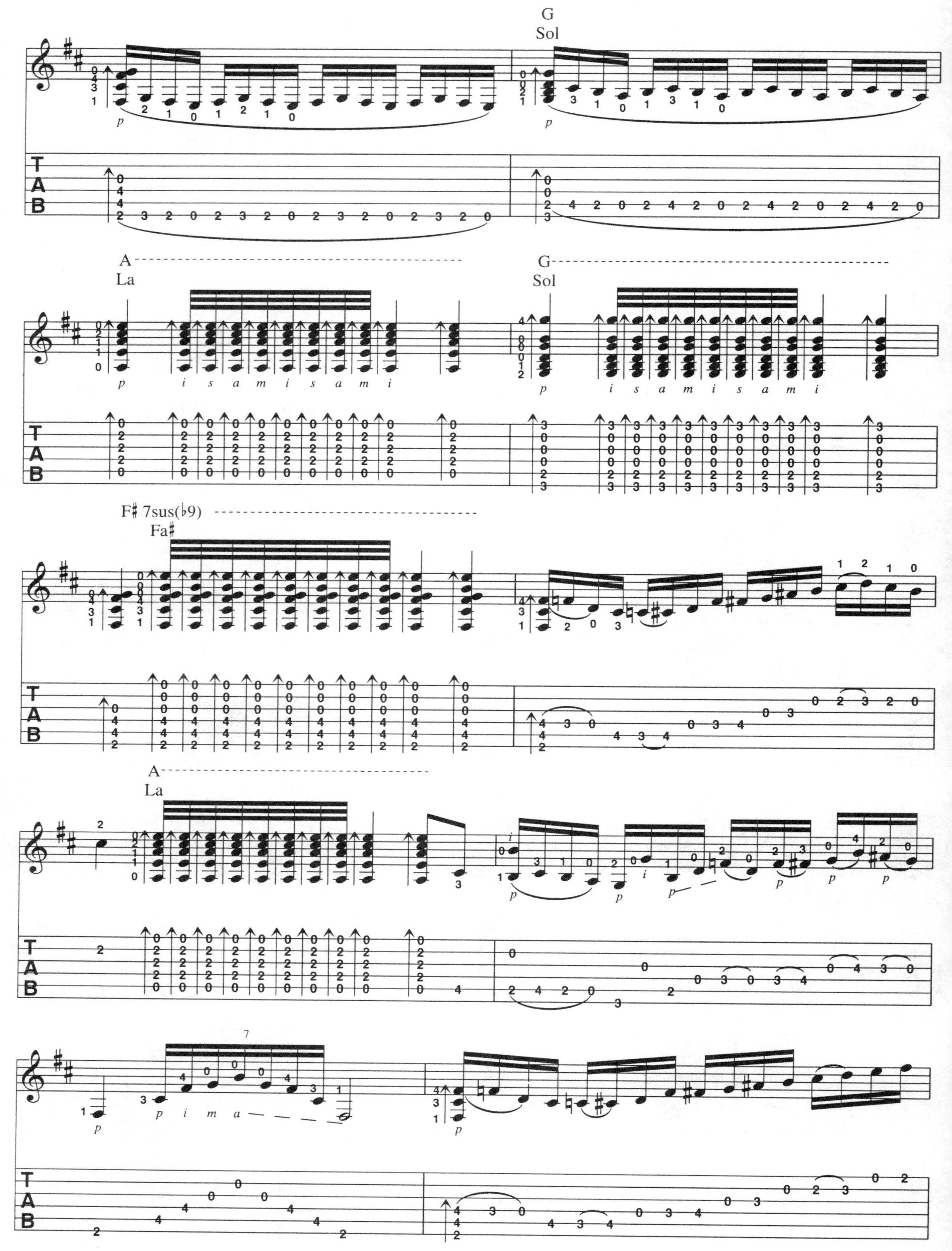
G
Sol
A
La
G
Sol
F♯ 7sus(♭9)
Fa♯
A
La

A
La
D
Re
G
Sol
F♯ 7
Fa♯
CII
E7
Mi
II

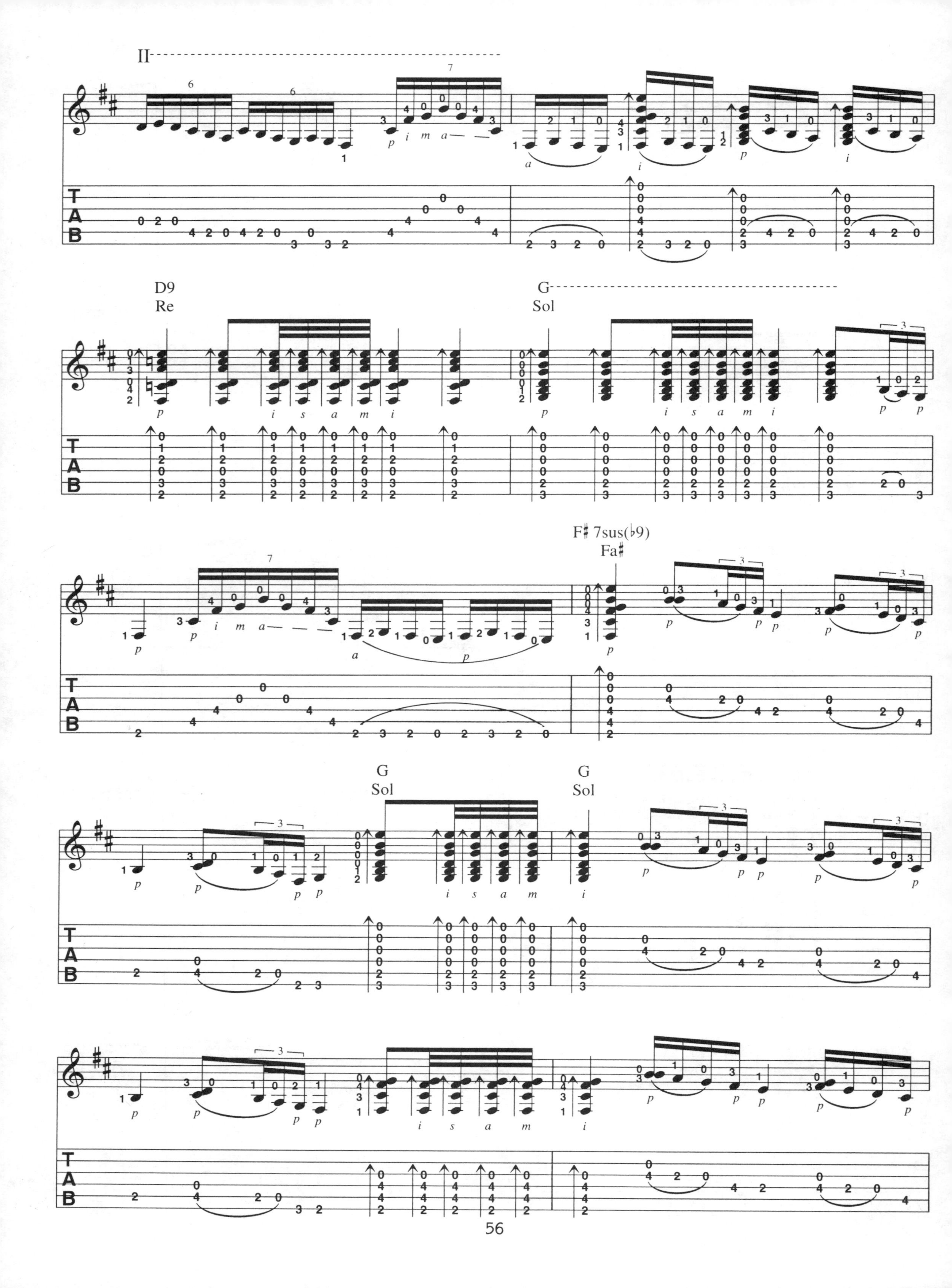
II
D9
Re
G
Sol
F♯ 7sus(♭9)
Fa♯
G
Sol
G
Sol

F♯ 7sus(♭9)
Fa♯
F♯ 7sus(♭9)
Fa♯
F♯ 7sus(♭9)
Fa♯
G
Sol

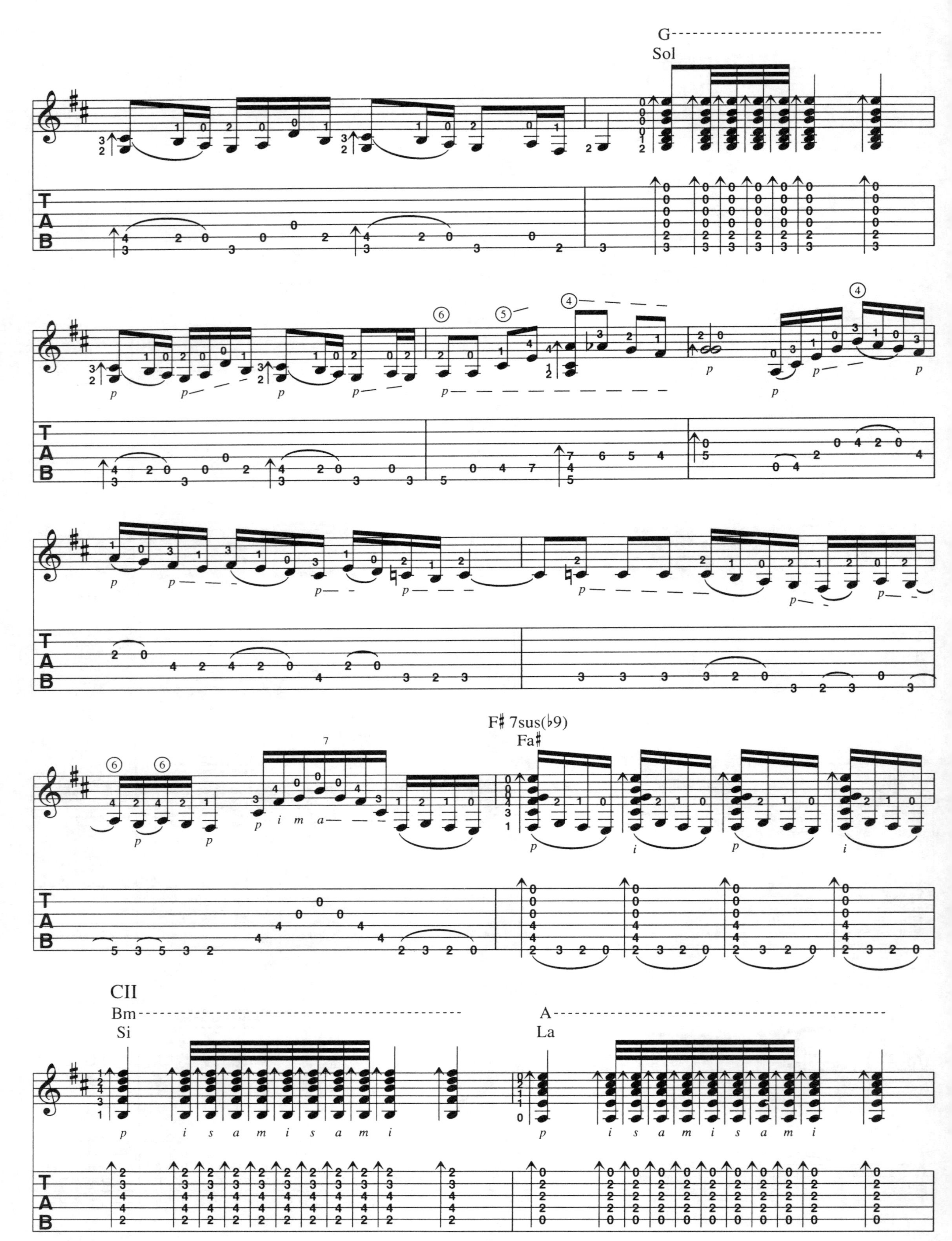
G
Sol
F♯ 7sus(♭9)
Fa♯
CII
Bm
Si
A
La

G
Sol
CII
F♯7sus(♭9)
Fa♯
G
Sol

MANTILLAS DE FERIA

6th String = D
5th String = G

Esteban de Sanlucar
Arr. by Juan Serrano

I
T
A
B

I
III
I
I
III
I
VII
D.S.
VII
V
VII
V
VII
VII

V VII VIII VII VIII
TAB
VII
TAB
VII
TAB
III
TAB
III VII XII VII III
TAB

CAPRICHO DE HUELVA
Fandangos

Symbol for the Spanish word "Golpe" ---- meaning to tap the top of the guitar only with the anular (a) fingertip.	G	Este símbolo significa "Golpe" y se toca dando un pequeño golpe con el dedo anular (a) en el golpeador de la guitarra.

Juan Serrano

CIII
CI
i m i m
E
G
A
G
G
G
F
E
G
G
A

G
G
F
E
CVII
E7
G
C
CI
CIII
CV
E7
CVII
G
CVIII
C

G
CVII
G
E7
G
CVIII
C
G
G

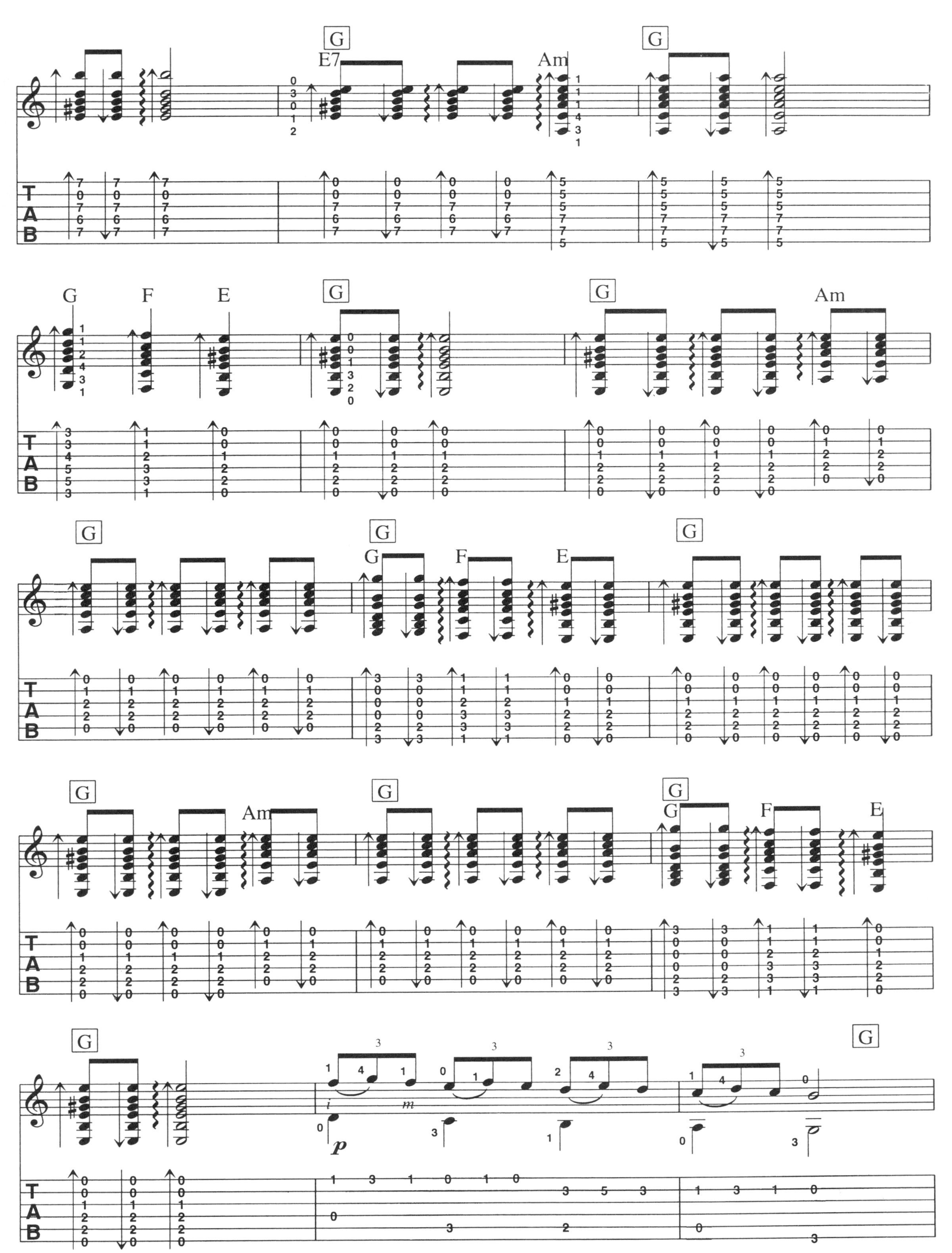
G
E7
Am
G
G
F
E
G
G
Am
G
G
G
F
E
G
G
Am
G
G
G
F
E
G
G
T
A
B

G
G
m i m
E♭9
G
Am
G
G
G F E
G
G
Am
G
G F E
T
A
B

G
C
F
C

CIII
G
C
E♭9
G
E
Am
G
G
G
F
E
G
G
Am

G
F
E
CV
CIII
G
CV
E
Am
CVII
G

CV
F
G
CVII
T
A
B

CV
F
G
E
Am
G
G
G
F
E
G
G
Am
G

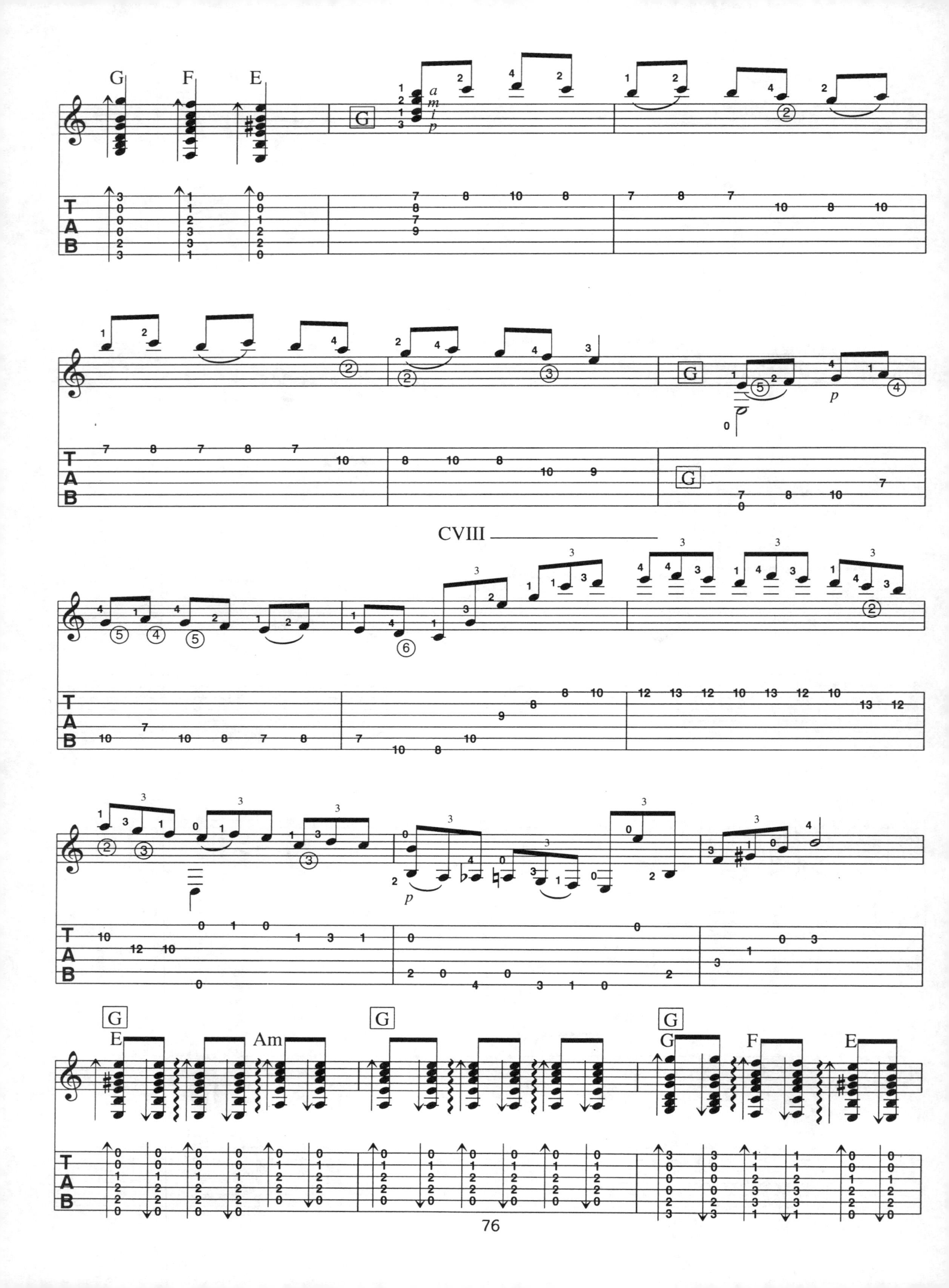
G
F
E
CVIII
Am
T
A
B

G
G
Am
G
G
F
E
G
E
G

E
G
Am
G
G
F
E
1/2 V
G
G7
F7
V
G7
G
III
F7
II
E7

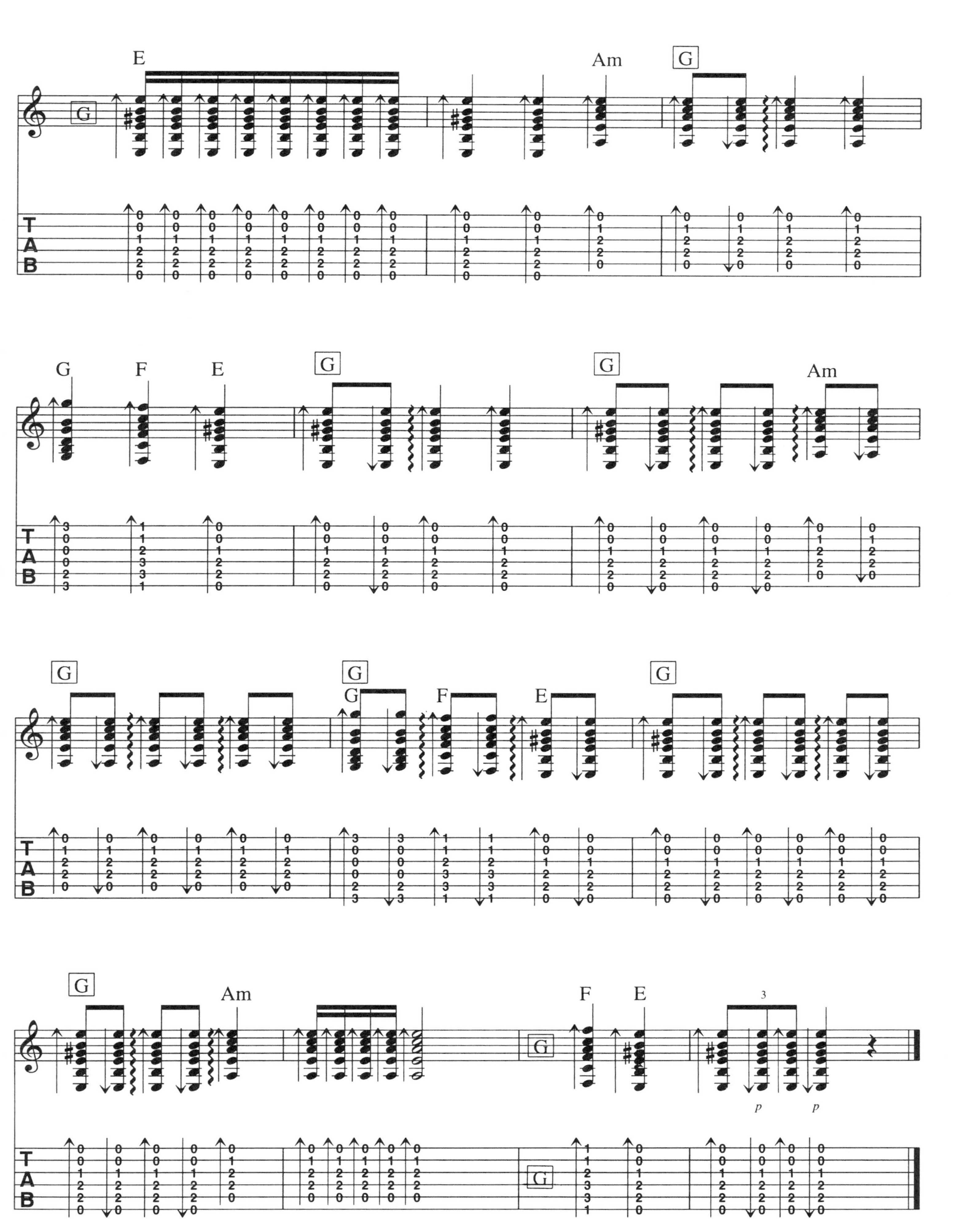
E
Am
G
G
TAB
G
F
E
G
G
Am
TAB
G
G
G
F
E
G
TAB
G
Am
F
E
G
3
p
p
TAB
G

ALMA
Bulerias in A minor

Symbol for the Spanish word "Golpe" ---- meaning to tap the top of the guitar only with the anular (a) fingertip.

G

Este símbolo significa "Golpe" y se toca dando un pequeño golpe con el dedo anular (a) en el golpeador de la guitarra.

Juan Serrano

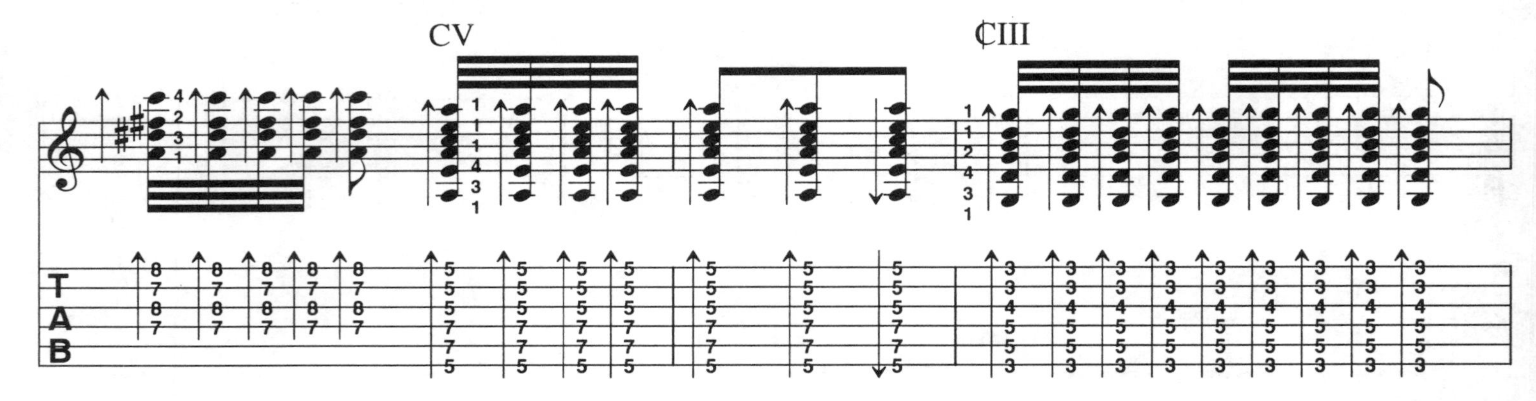

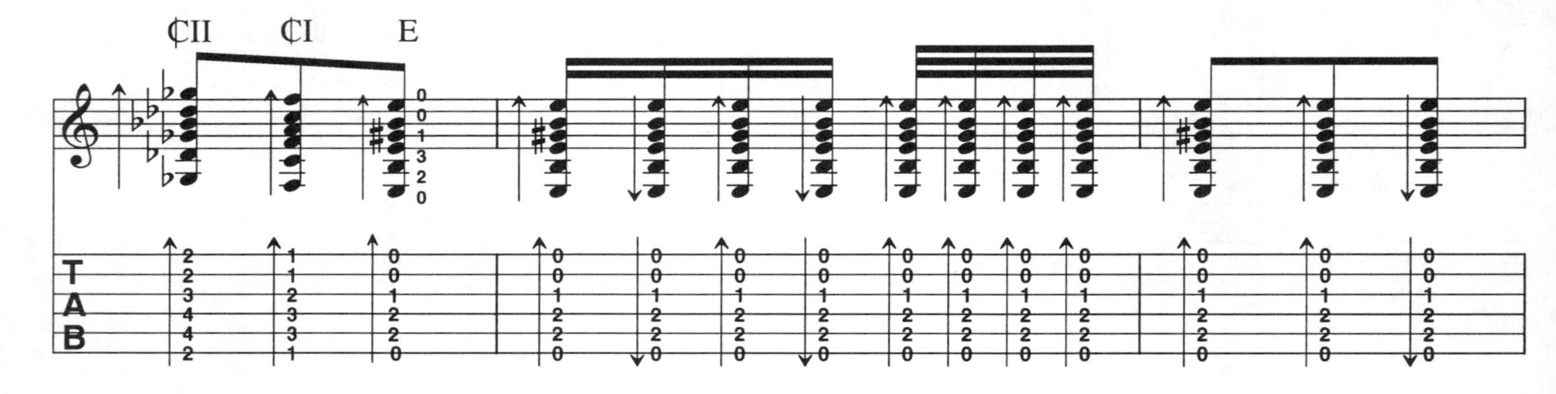

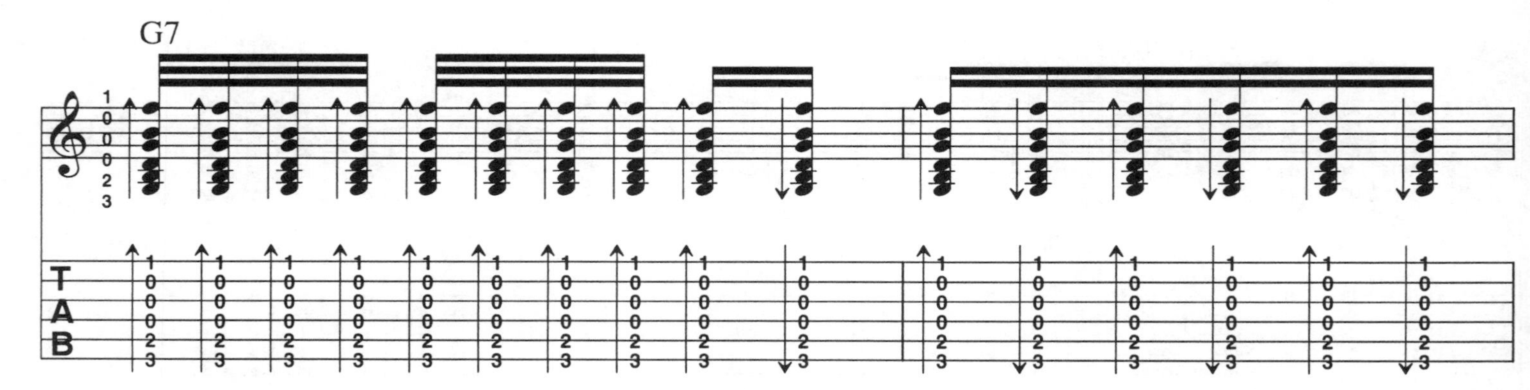

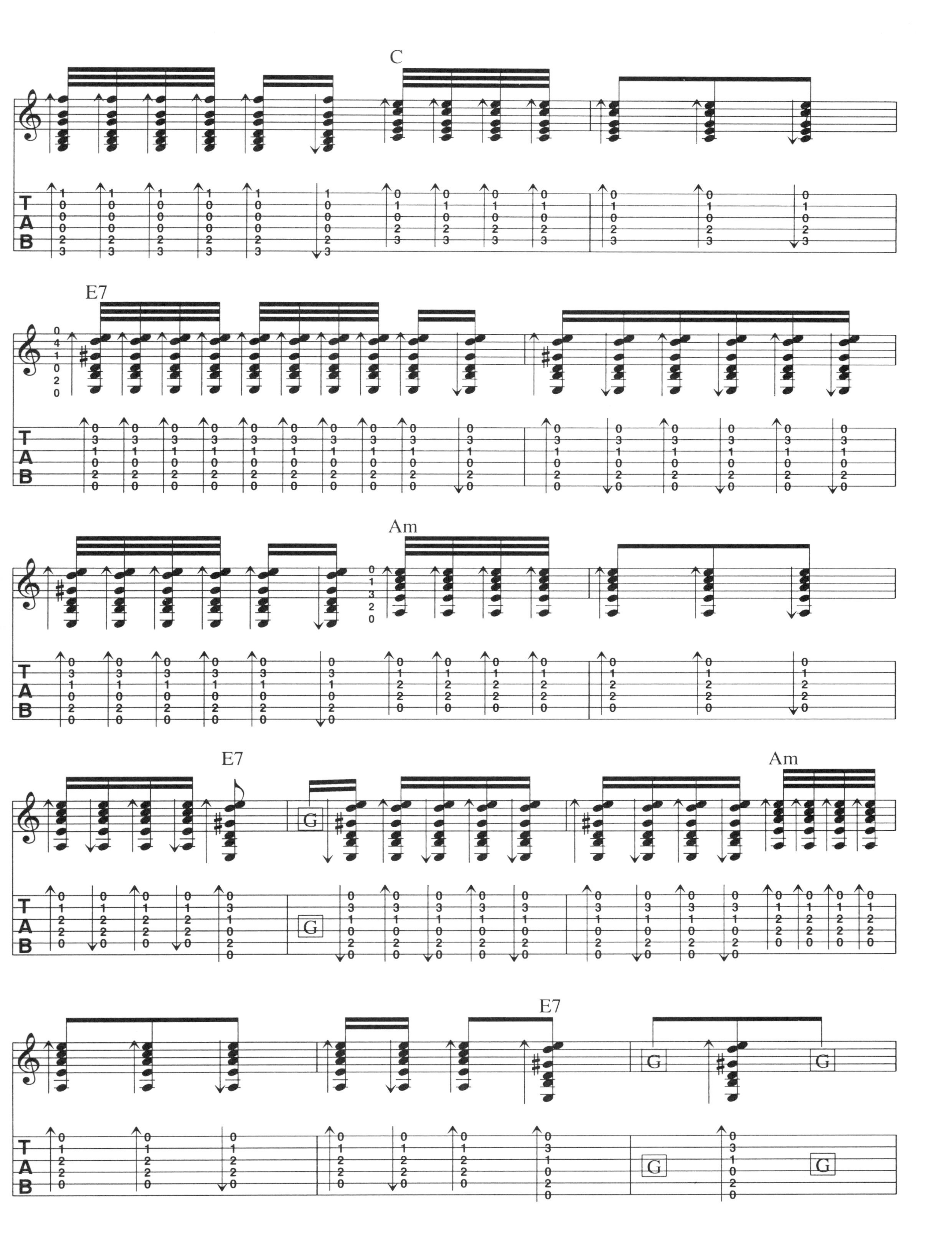
C
E7
Am
E7
Am
E7
G
G
G
G
G
T
A
B

Am
E
Am

E7
E7

C
G7
C
CV
p
G
G

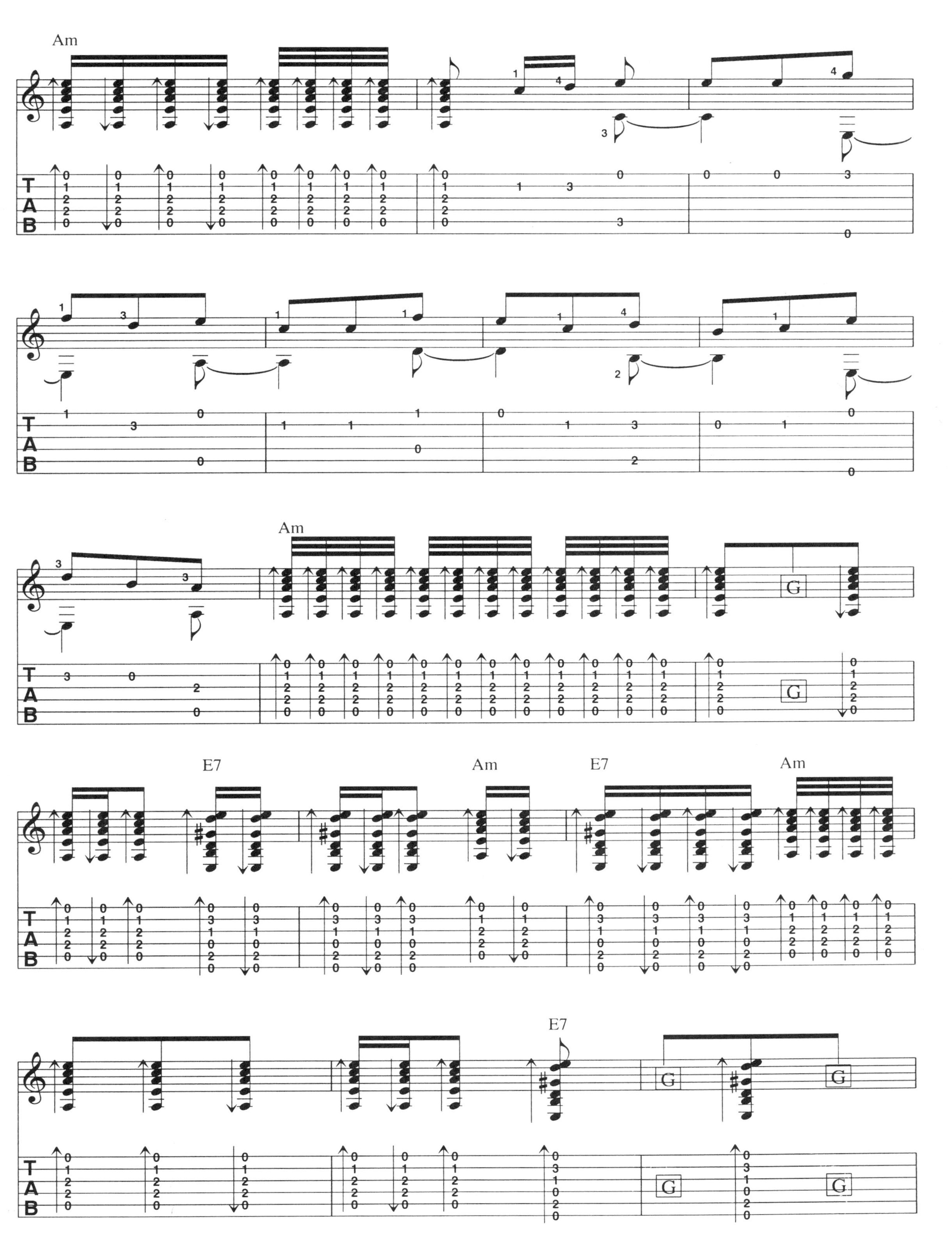
Am
Am
G
G
E7
Am
E7
Am
E7
G
G

Am
G
p
TAB
Am
G
p
E7
G
E7
G
p
Am
G
p
G
Dm
G
i m i m i m
i m i m i m

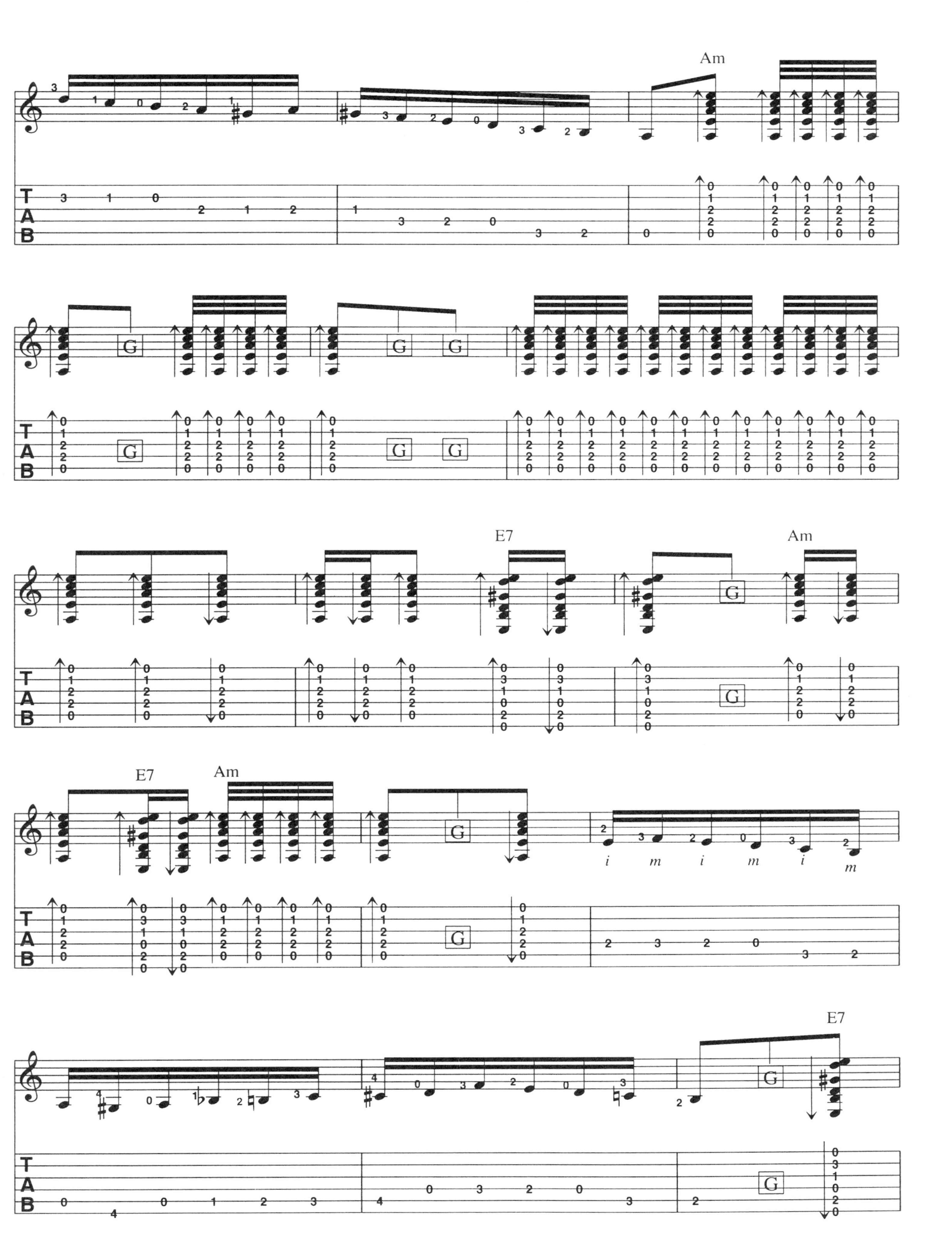
Am
E7
Am
E7
Am
E7

m i m i m i
m i m i m i
Am
E7
Am
E7
Am

p p i m a
i m i m i m
G G
p p i m a
i m i m i m
Am
G
Dm
G
TAB

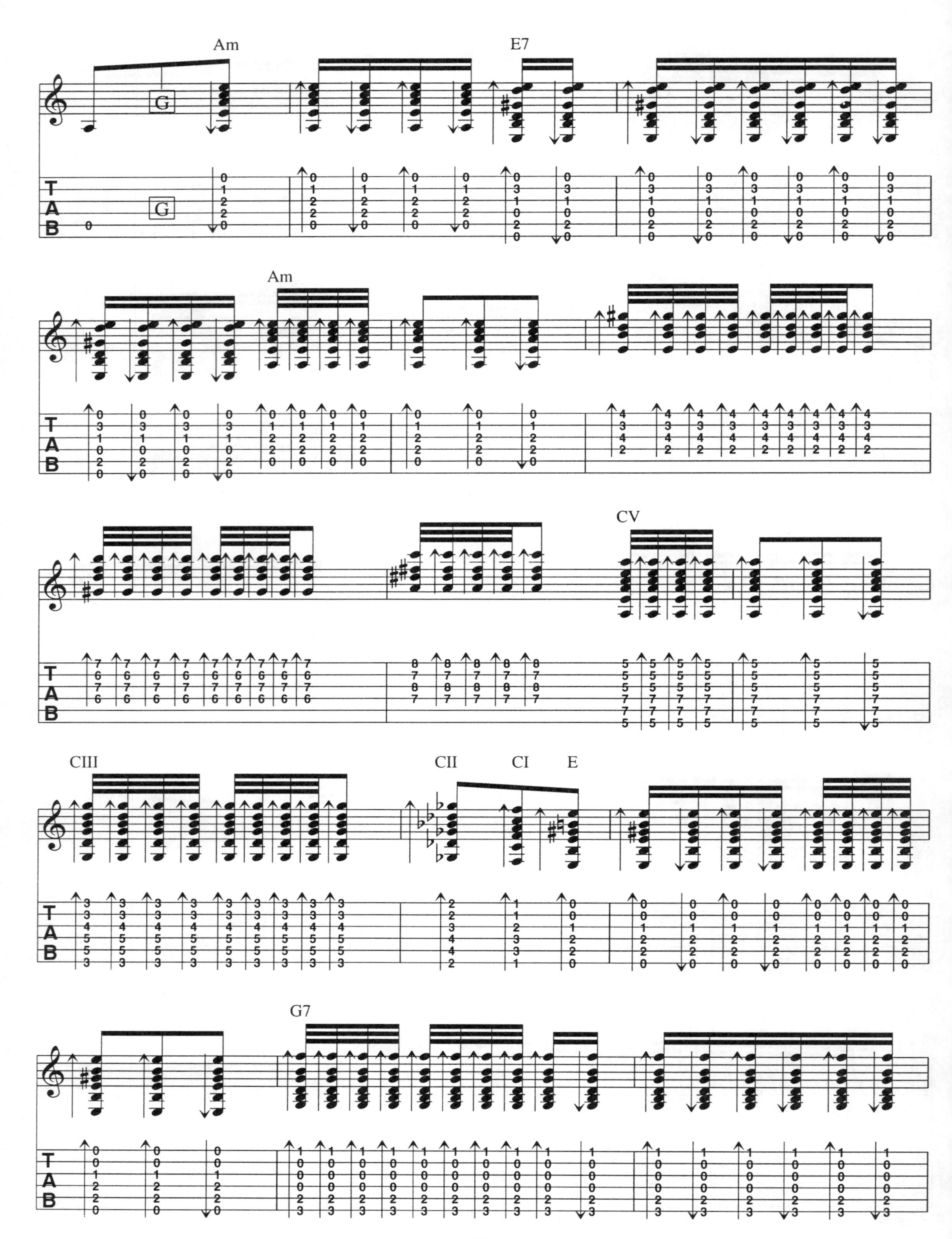
Am
E7
G
T
A
B
Am
CV
CIII
CII
CI
E
G7

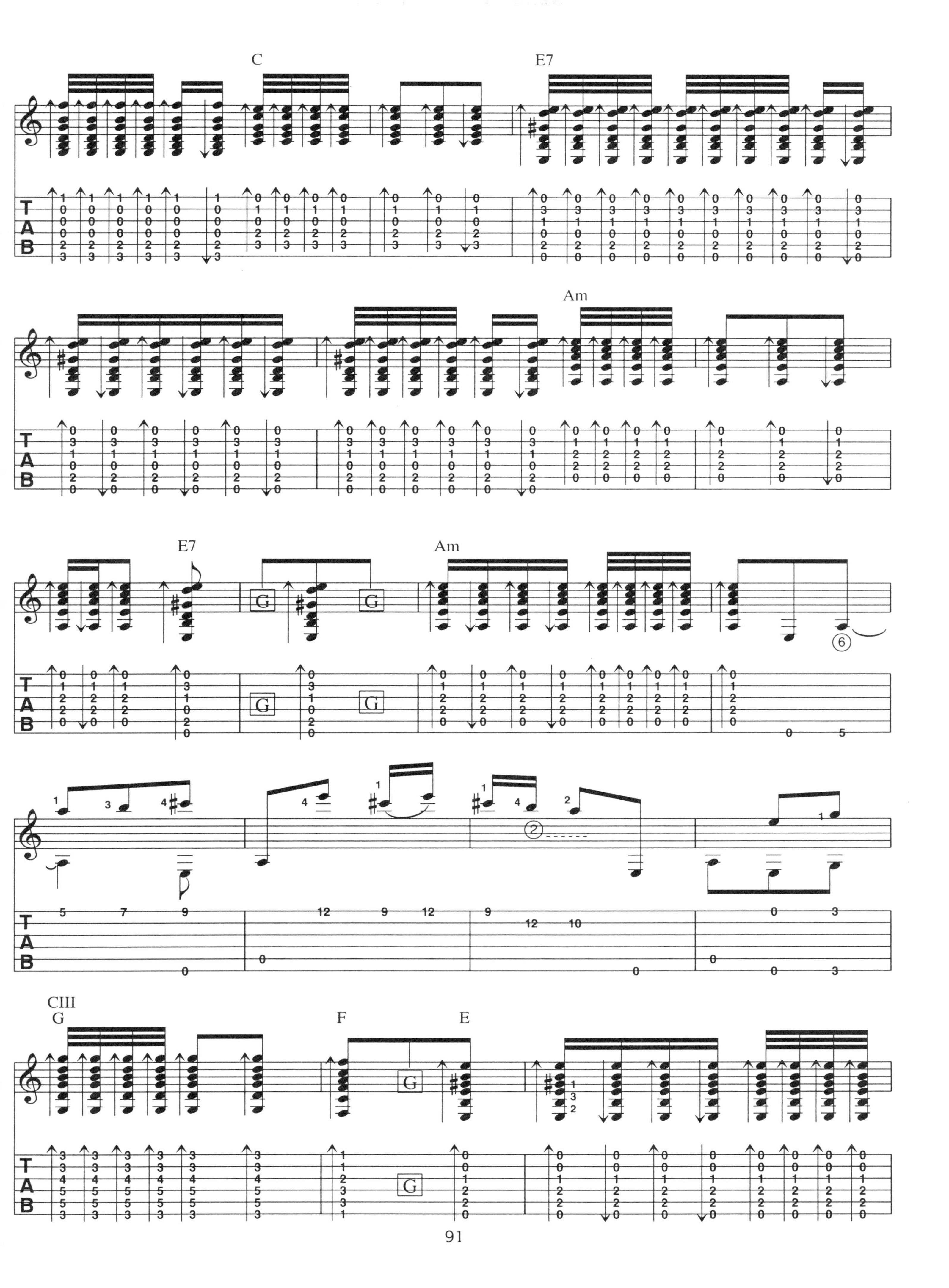
C
E7
TAB
Am
E7
G
Am
CIII
G
F
E

CIII
G
F
E
D
TAB

G
CV
Am
p
i
m
a
m
CIII

CVII
CVIII
G
G
CI
G
G

VII
Am
G
CV

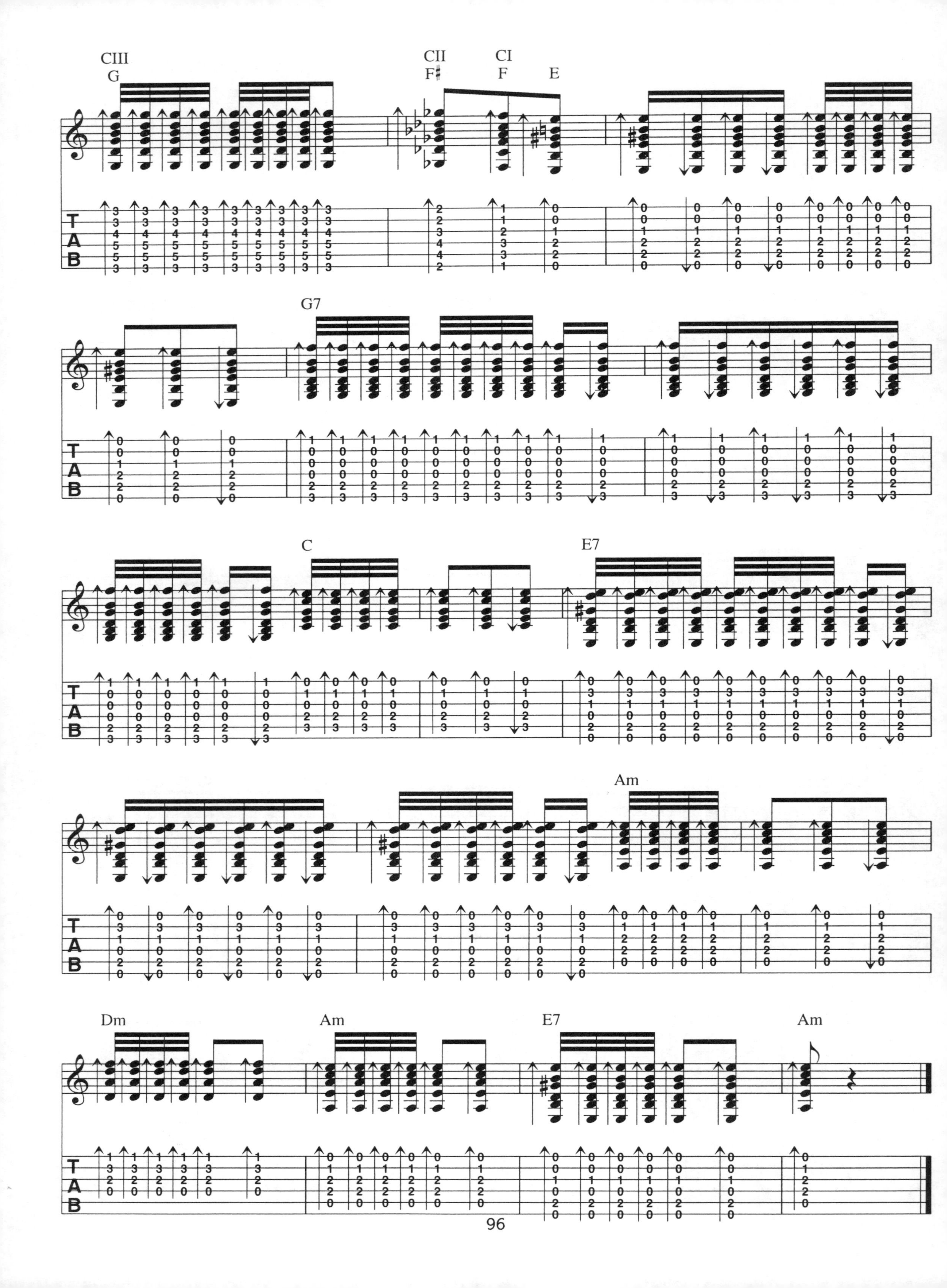
CIII
G
CII
F♯
CI
F
E
G7
C
E7
Am
Dm
Am
E7
Am
T
A
B

ANDALUCIAN DANCE
Tanguillo

Symbol for the Spanish word "Golpe"---- meaning to tap the top of the guitar only with the anular (a) fingertip.	G	Este símbolo significa "Golpe" y se toca dando un pequeño golpe con el dedo anular (a) en el golpeador de la guitarra.

Juan Serrano

G
E
E
E
E7
E
CV
E
A
TAB

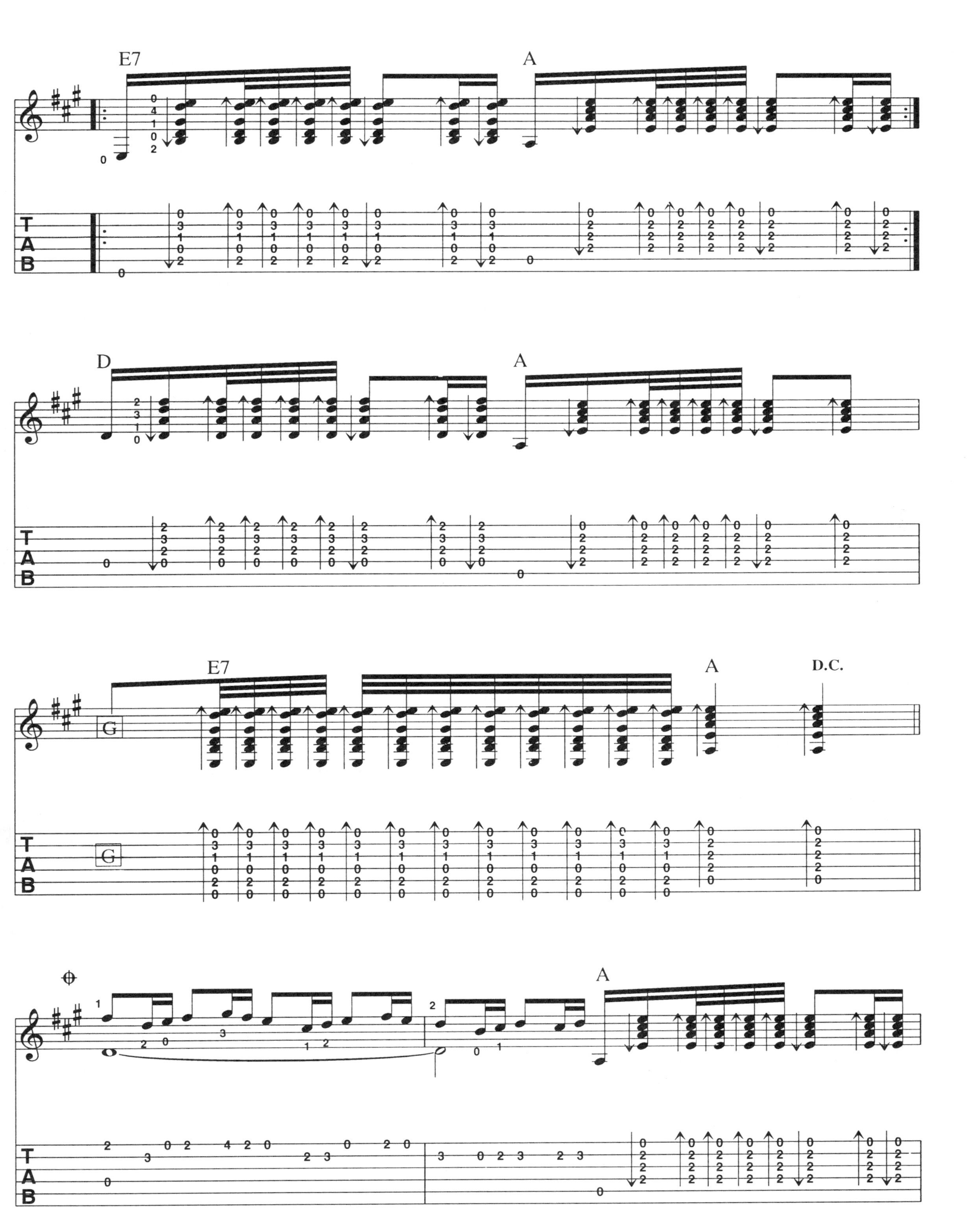
E7
A
D
A
G
E7
A
D.C.
G
A

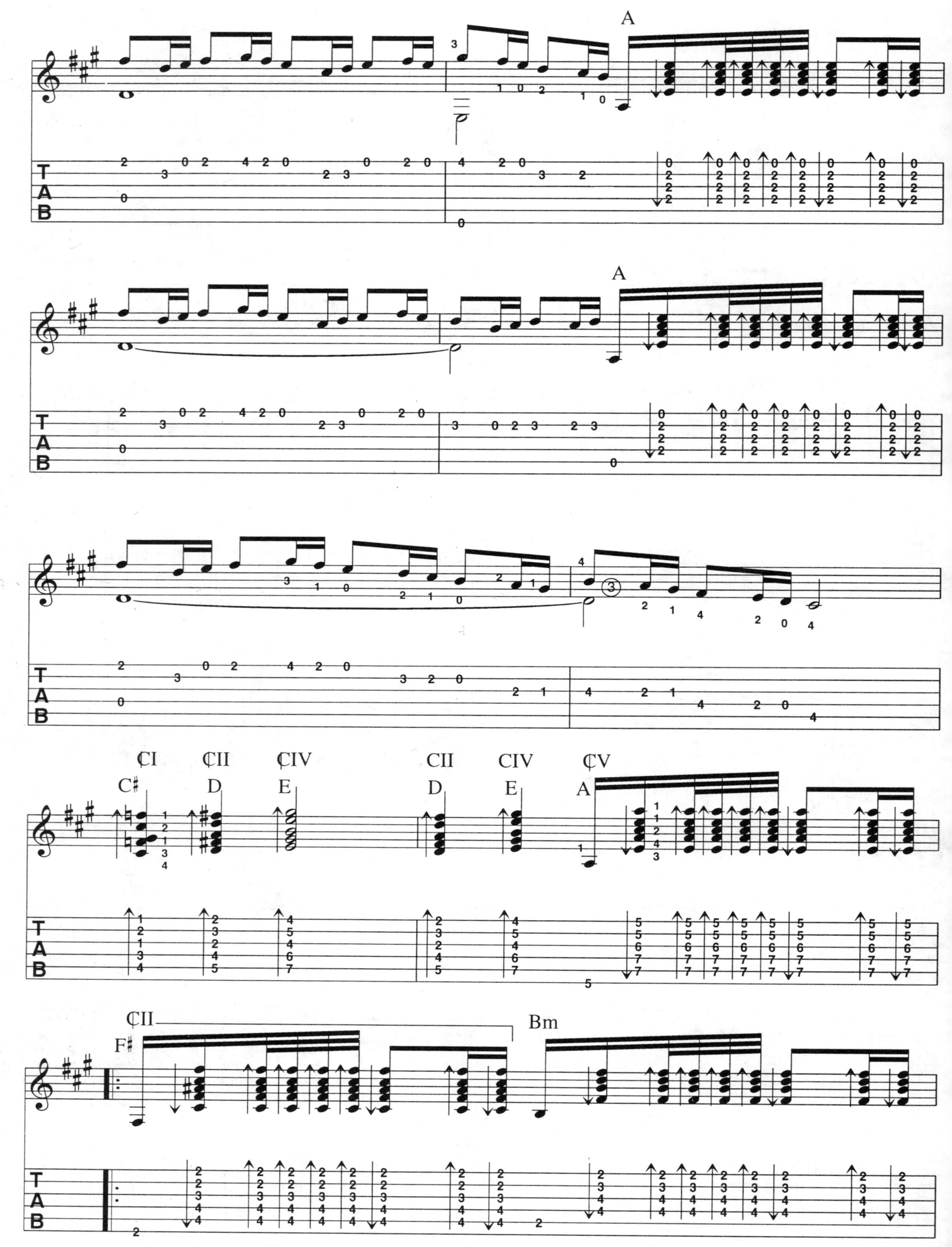
A
TAB
A
TAB
TAB
ȻI
ȻII
ȻIV
CII
CIV
ȻV
C♯
D
E
D
E
A
TAB
ȻII
F♯
Bm
TAB

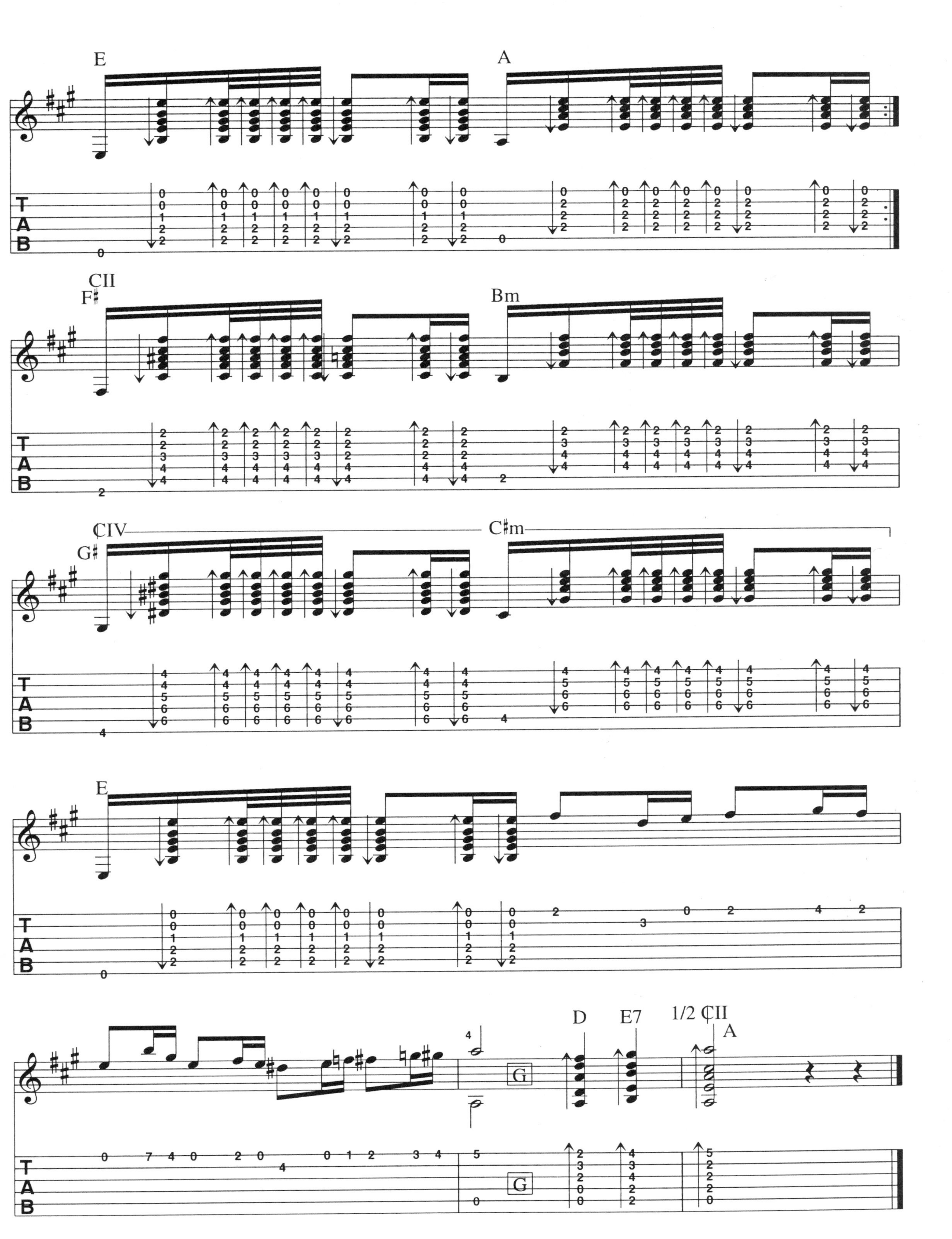
E
A
CII
F♯
Bm
CIV
G♯
C♯m
E
D
E7
1/2 CII
A
G
TAB

BLAZING GUITAR
Rumba

This symbol is played by crossing the right hand over the six strings at the lower end of the finger board and the tips of the fingers produce a soft stroke on the sounding board of the guitar	(T)	Este símbolo se toca atra - vesando la mano derecha sobre las seis cuerdas en la parte final del diapasón y que las puntas de los dedos den un pequeño golpe en la tapa.

Juan Serrano

Am
Am
Dm
E7
F7
Am
Am
Dm

G
CIII
Fdim.
Fdim.
G♯dim.
Am
CV
G7 V
V
C
E7
T
A
B

Am
Am
Am
Am
Dm
E7
F7
Am
E
F CI
G CIII

Fdim.
Fdim.
G♯dim.
Am
CV
p
T
TAB
Am
Am

Am
p
Am
p
Am
p
E7
p
p
Am
p
T
A
B

Am
Dm
Am

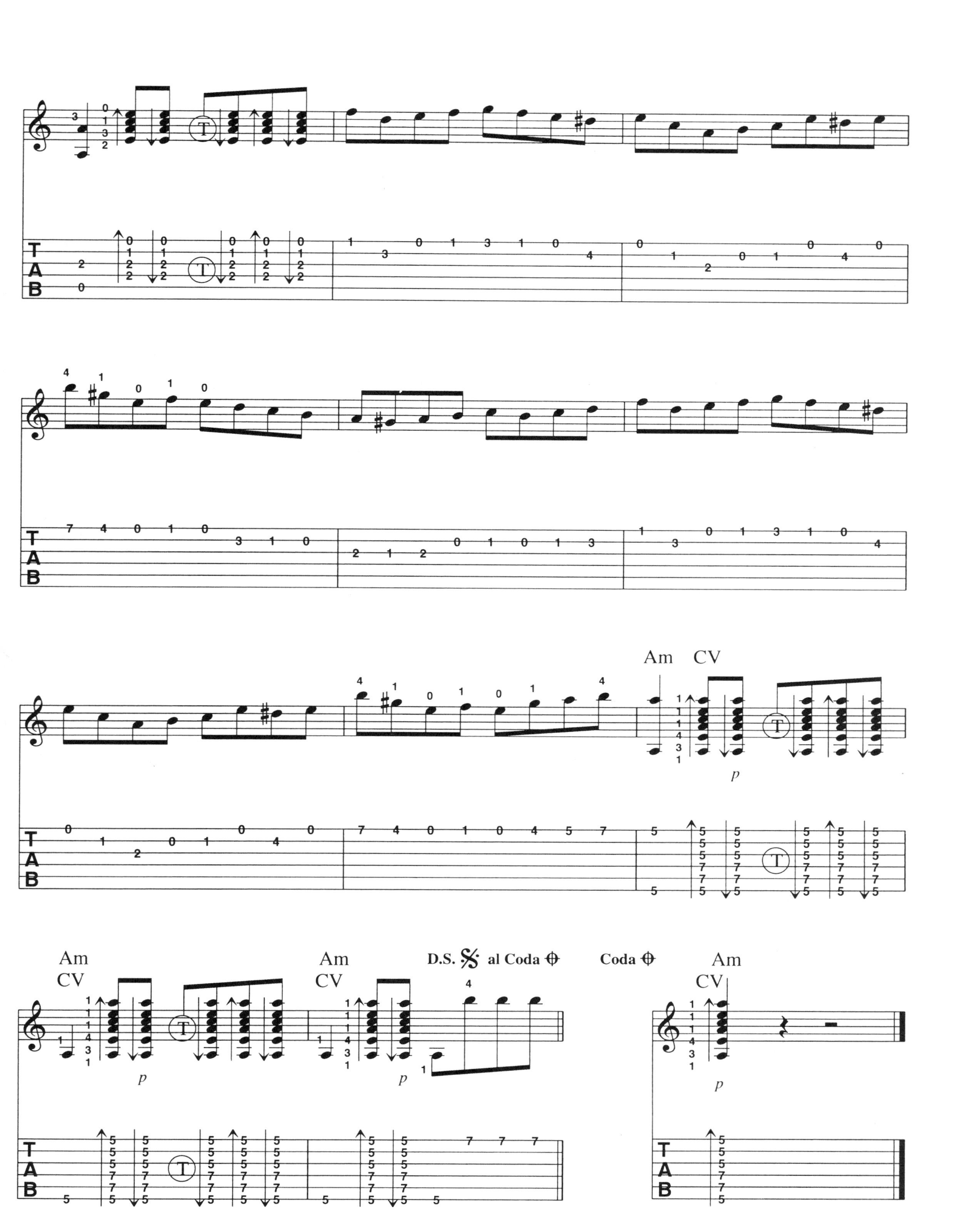
Am
CV
Am
CV
Am
CV
D.S. 𝄋 al Coda ⊕
Coda ⊕
Am
CV

MEMORY OF LOVE
Bolero

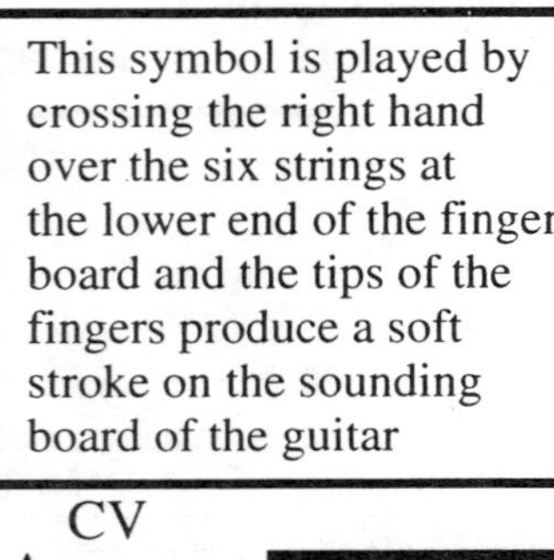

This symbol is played by crossing the right hand over the six strings at the lower end of the finger board and the tips of the fingers produce a soft stroke on the sounding board of the guitar

Ⓣ

Este símbolo se toca atra - vesando la mano derecha sobre las seis cuerdas en la parte final del diapasón y que las puntas de los dedos den un pequeño golpe en la tapa.

Juan Serrano

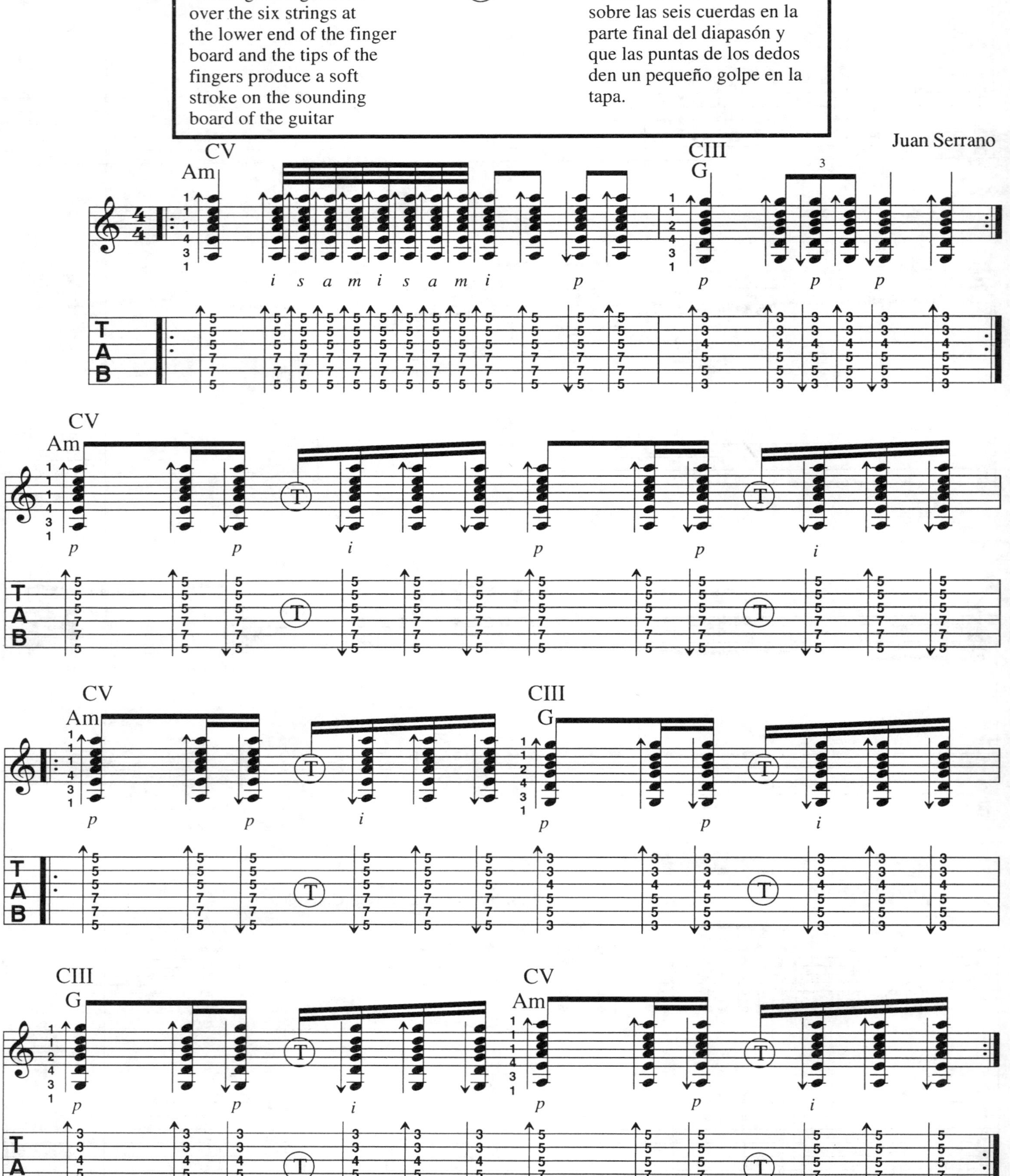

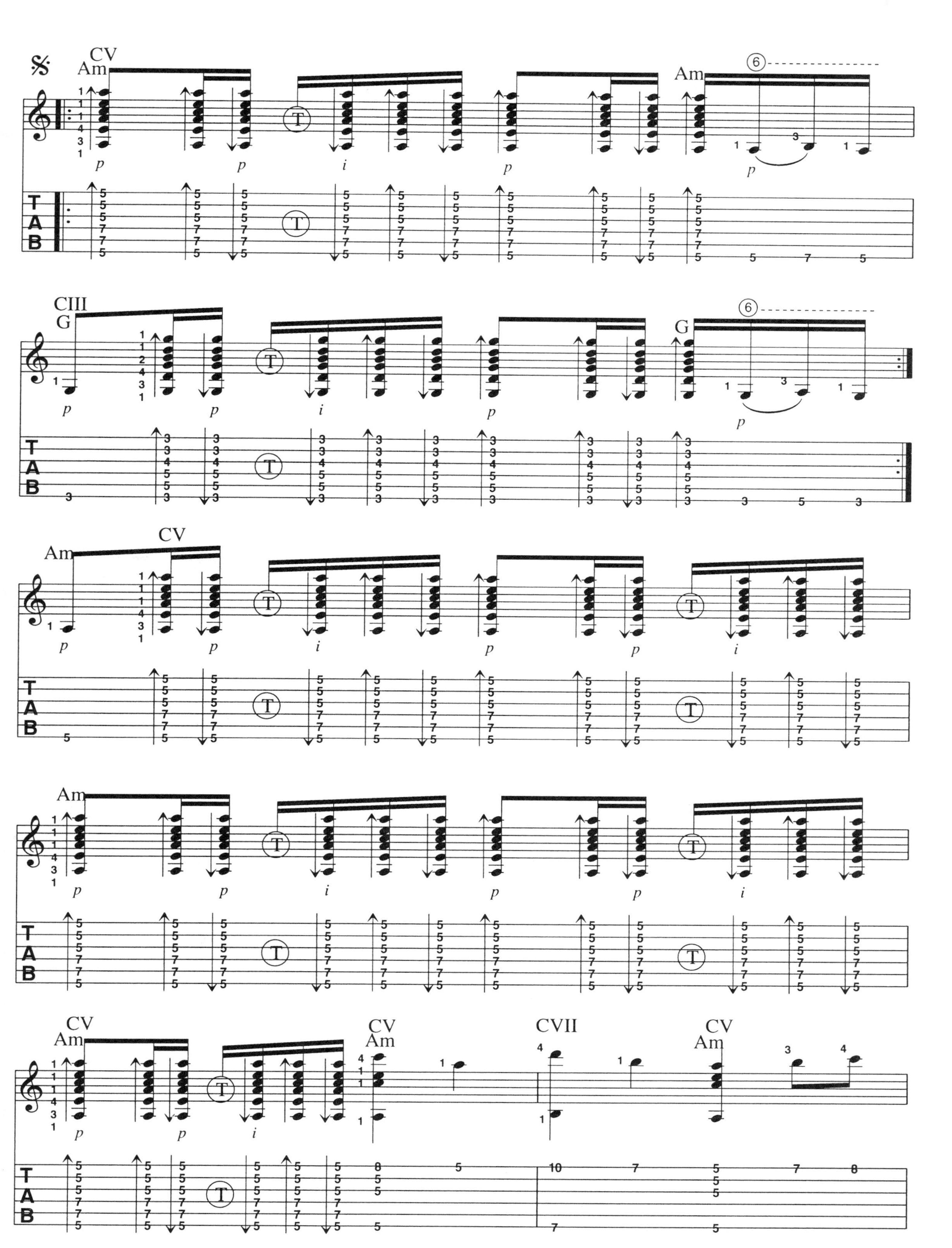
CV
Am
CIII
G
CV
Am
Am
CV
Am
CV
Am
CVII
CV
Am
T
A
B

E7
p i p p i
E7
Am CV
G CIII
F CI
p p i
E
p i p p i
E
AmCV
CVII
Am CV
p i
E7
p i p p i
T
A
B

CIII
G
CV
Am
CIX
E
T
p
i
Am
E7
Am
E7
Am
Am
Am
Am

Am
CIII
G
AmCV
AmCV
CV
CVII
G CIII
F CI
F
F CI
CV
E7
Am6
E7♭9
Am6
E7♭9

CV
Am
Am
CV
Am
CVII
G
CVII
G
V
CV
F
CV
F
CV
F
C
C

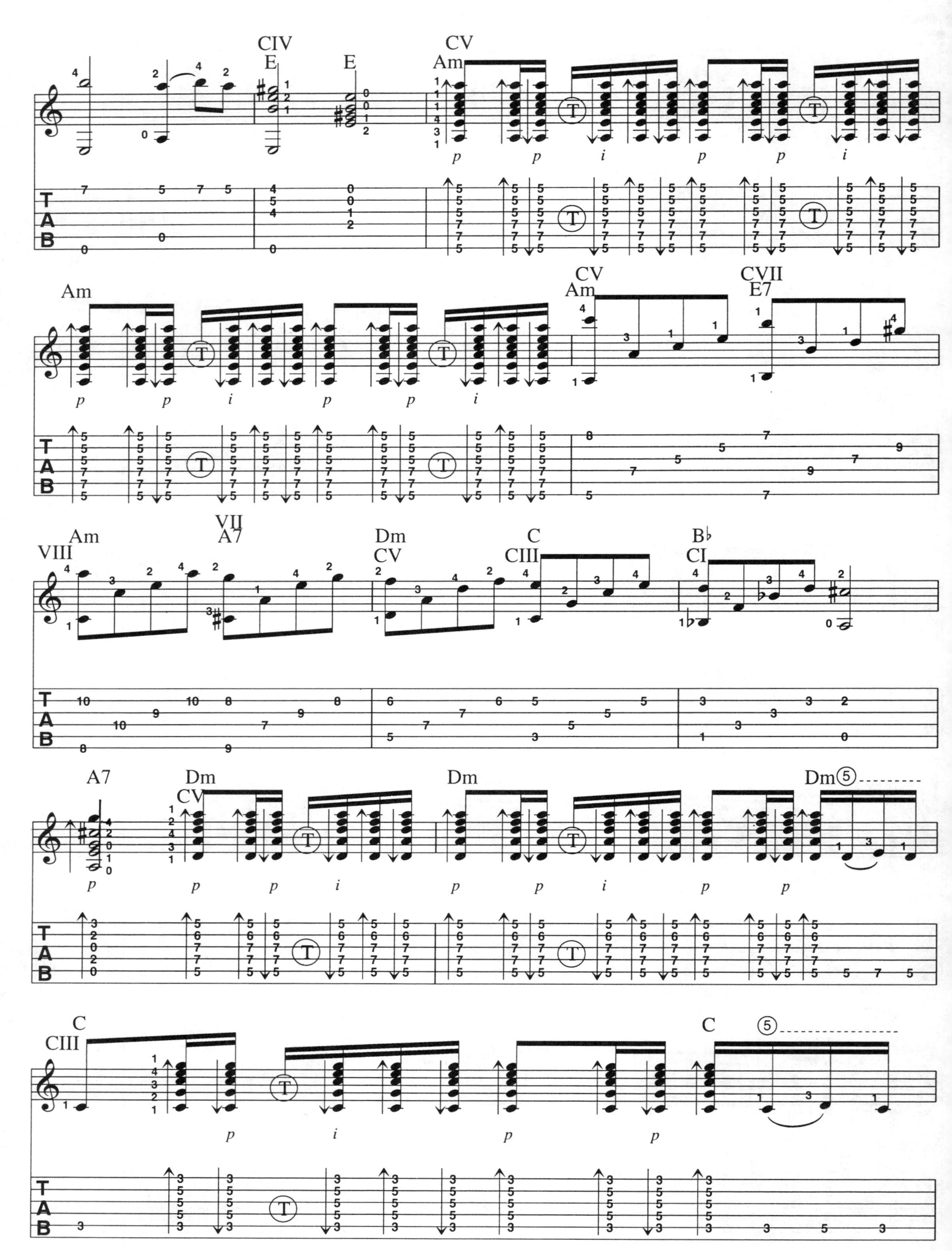
CIV
E
E
CV
Am
Am
CV
Am
CVII
E7
VIII
Am
VII
A7
Dm
CV
C
CIII
B♭
CI
A7
Dm
CV
Dm
Dm ⑤
C
CIII
C
⑤

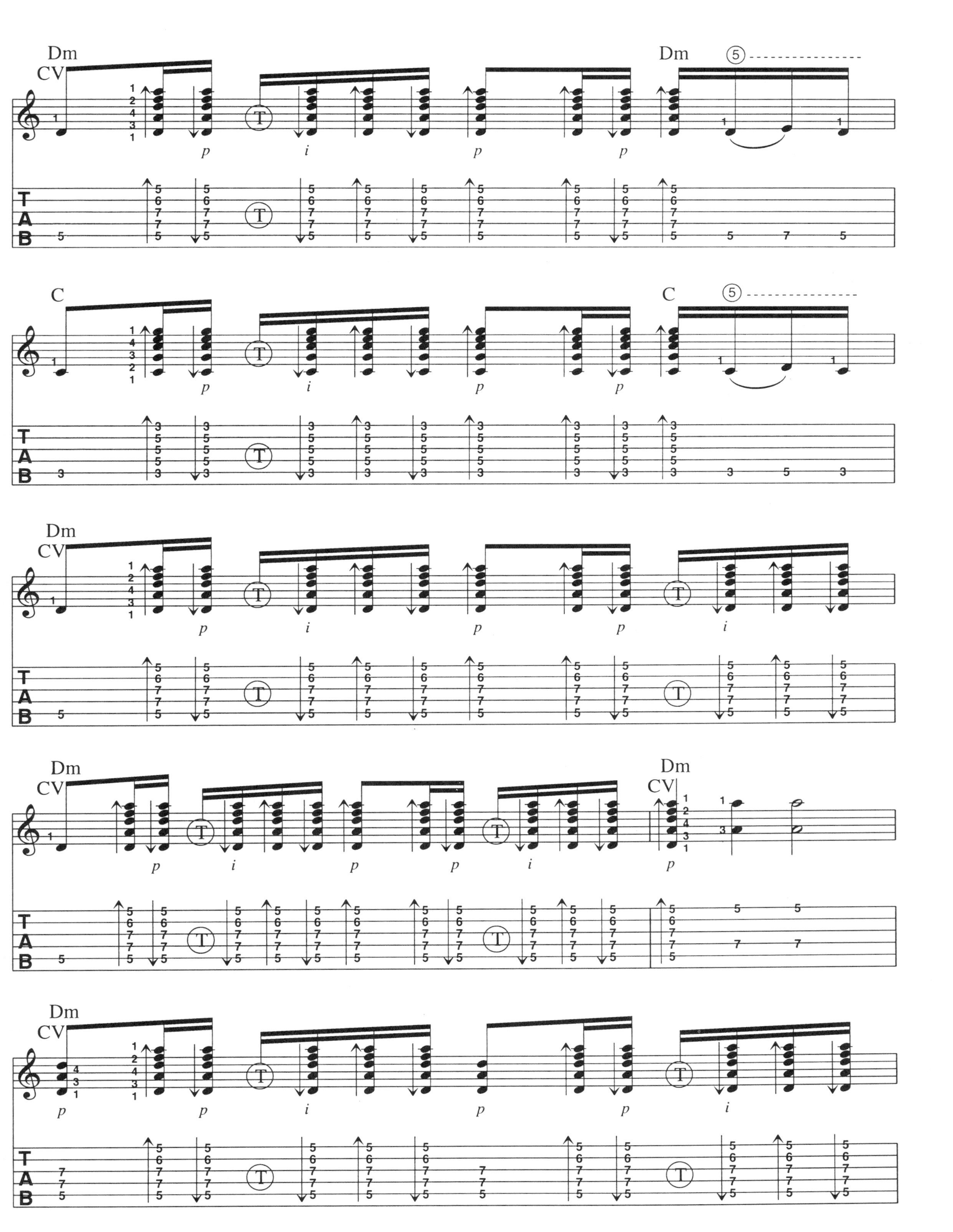
Dm
CV
Dm
C
C
Dm
CV
Dm
CV
Dm
CV
Dm
CV
T
A
B

V
III
CIII C
C
CIII
C
CIII
III
B♭
CI
B♭
CI
B♭
CI
A
CII
A7
Dm
Dm
C
B♭

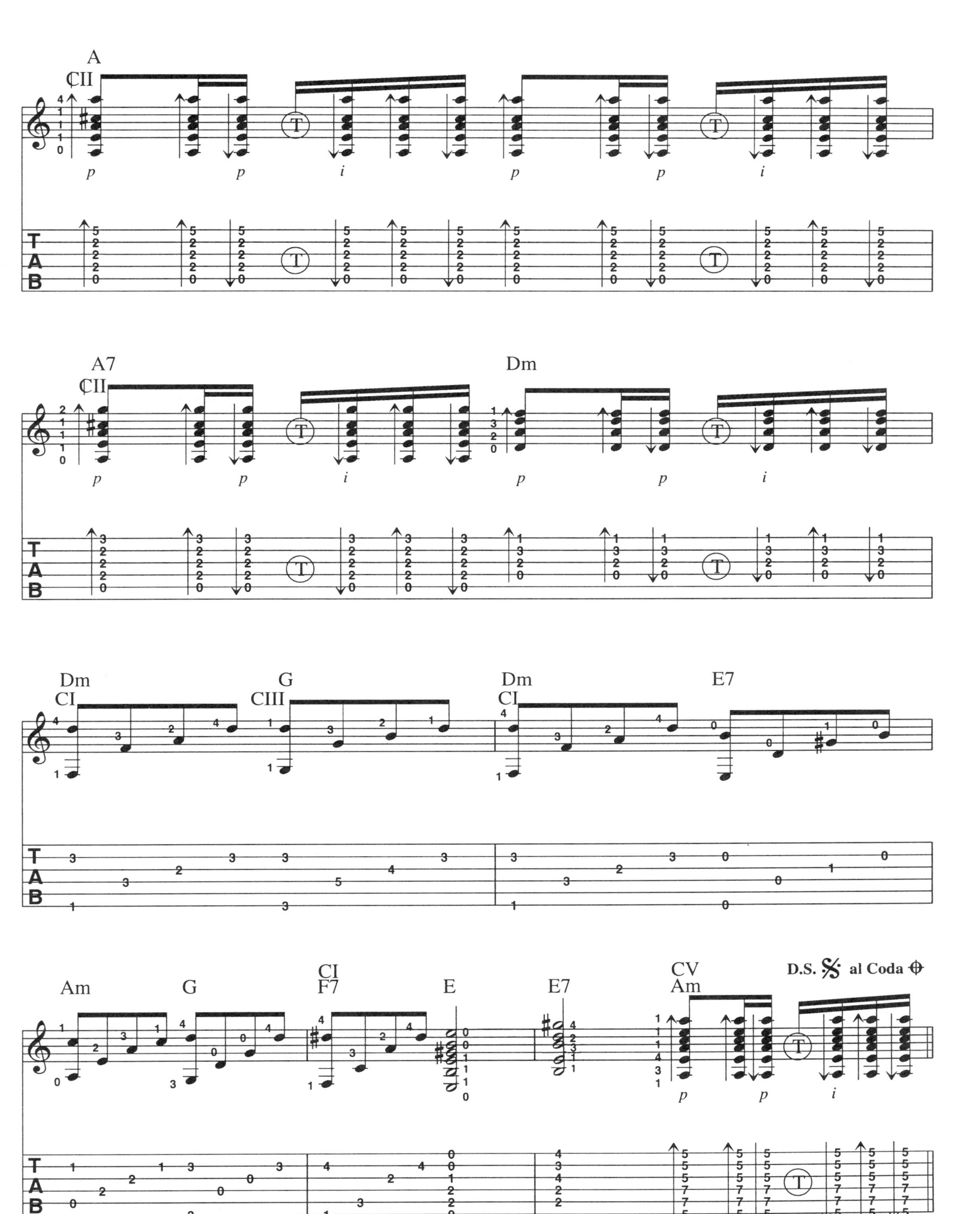
A
CII
p p i p p i
A7
CII
Dm
Dm
CI
G
CIII
Dm
CI
E7
Am
G
CI
F7
E
E7
CV
Am
D.S. al Coda

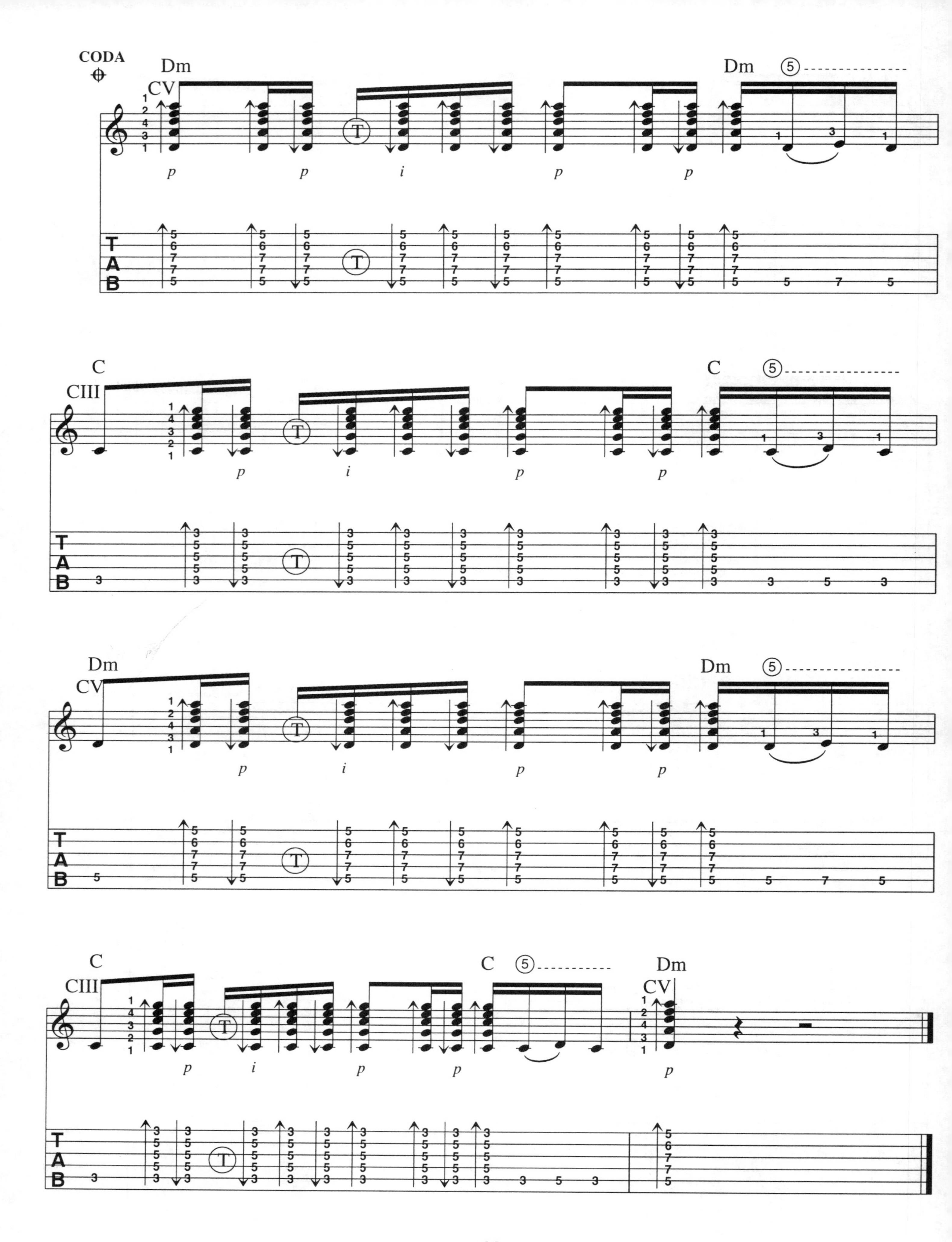
CODA
Dm
CV
Dm
C
CIII
C
Dm
CV
Dm
C
CIII
C
Dm
CV
p
i
T
TAB

ANA MARIA
Tientos

Juan Serrano

B♭
(Si♭)
Gm6
(Sol)
B♭
(Si♭)
B♭
(Si♭)
A
(La)
B♭
(Si♭)
A
(La)
A
(La)
CIII
B♭maj7
(Si♭)
CIII
Gm
(Sol)
C♯ dim
(Do♯)
CVI
B♭
(Si♭)
A
(La)
CX
B♭
(Si♭)
A
(La)
TAB

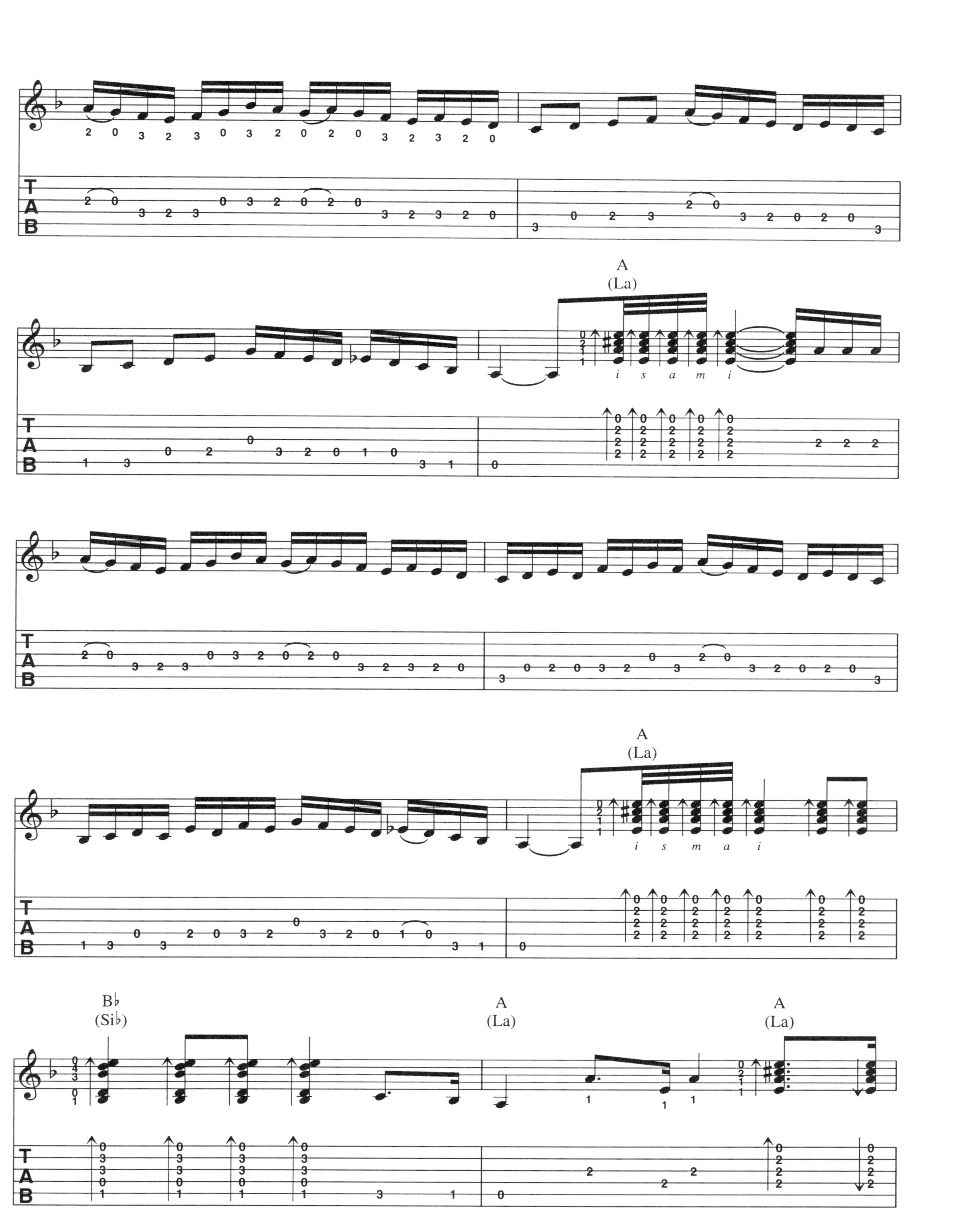
A
(La)
i s a m i
A
(La)
i s m a i
B♭
(Si♭)
A
(La)
A
(La)

CII
A
(La)
CIII
Gm
(Sol)
CV
CVI
B♭
(Si♭)
CX
IX
Dm
(Re)
C
(Do)
A7(♭9)
A7
T
A
B

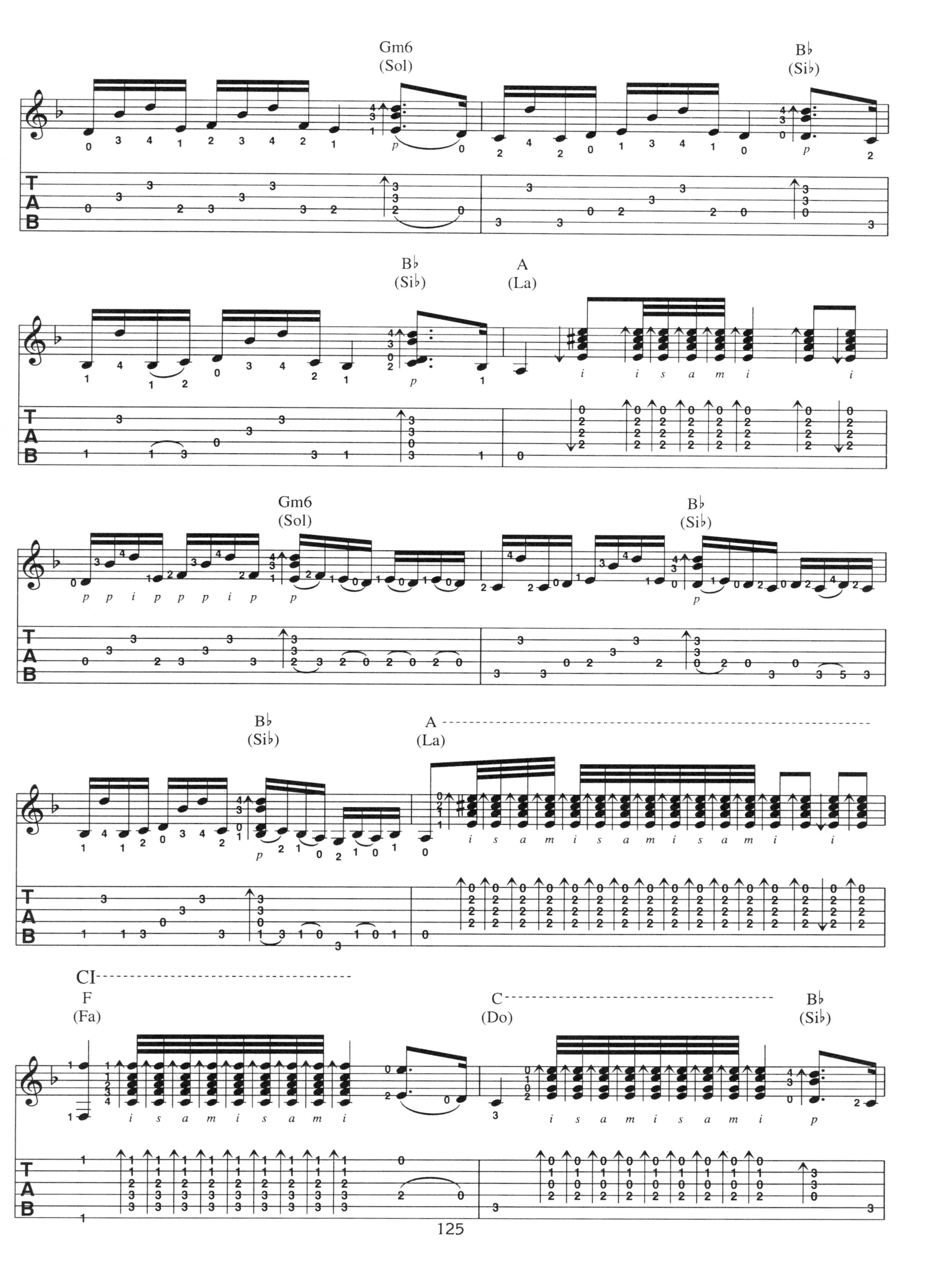
Gm6
(Sol)
B♭
(Si♭)
B♭
(Si♭)
A
(La)
Gm6
(Sol)
B♭
(Si♭)
B♭
(Si♭)
A
(La)
CI
F
(Fa)
C
(Do)
B♭
(Si♭)

B♭ (Si♭)
A7 (La)
A (La)
A7 (La)
Gm6 (Sol)
A7 (La)
A7 (La)
¢II
A7 (La)
A (La)
A7 (La)
A7 (La)
Dm (Re)
TAB

C
(Do)
B♭
(Si♭)
A
(La)
Dm
(Re)
C
(Do)
B♭
(Si♭)
B♭
(Si♭)
B♭
(Si♭)
Gm6
(Sol)
A
(La)
F
(Fa)
T
A
B

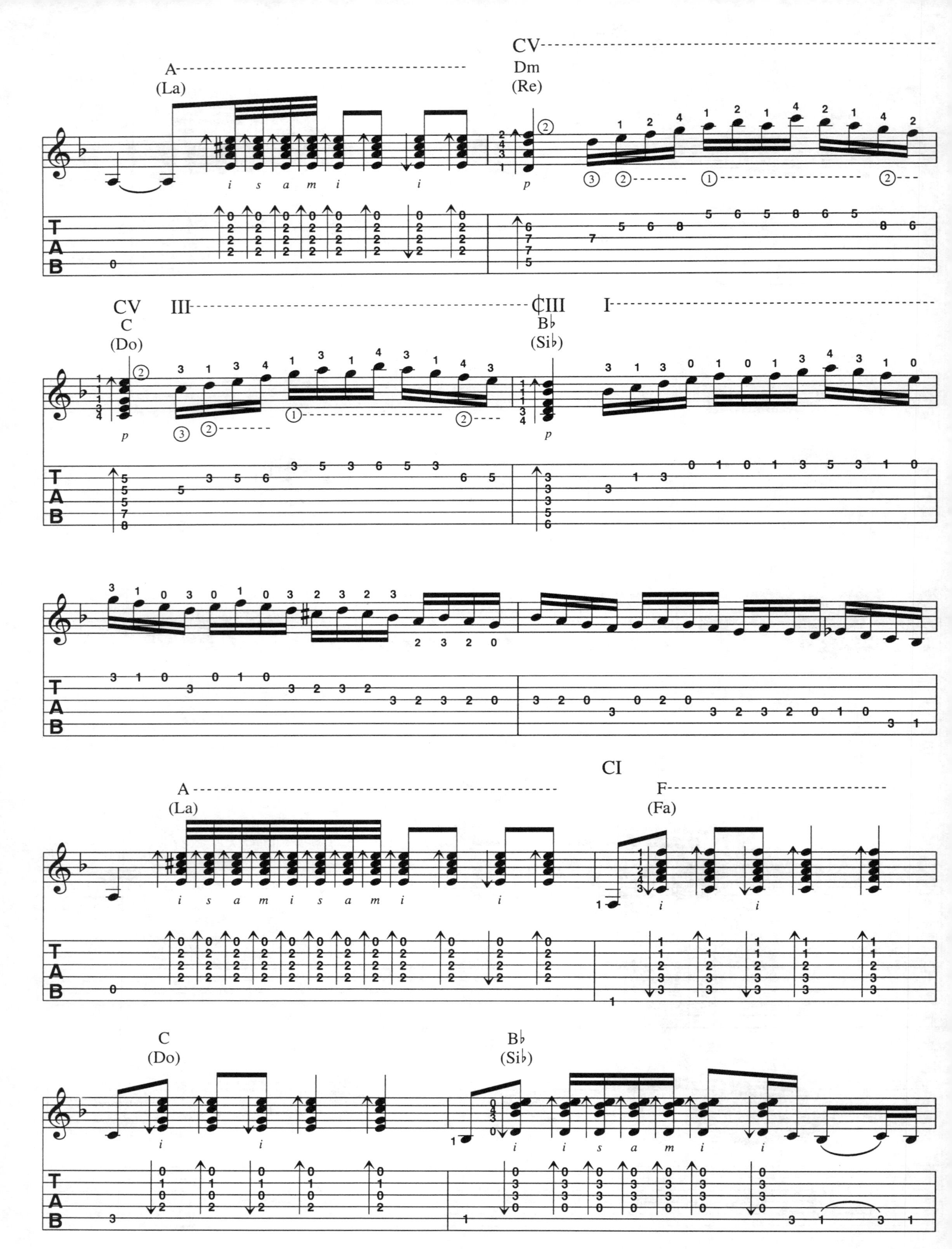
A (La)
CV
Dm (Re)
CV
C (Do)
III
CIII
B♭ (Si♭)
I
A (La)
CI
F (Fa)
C (Do)
B♭ (Si♭)

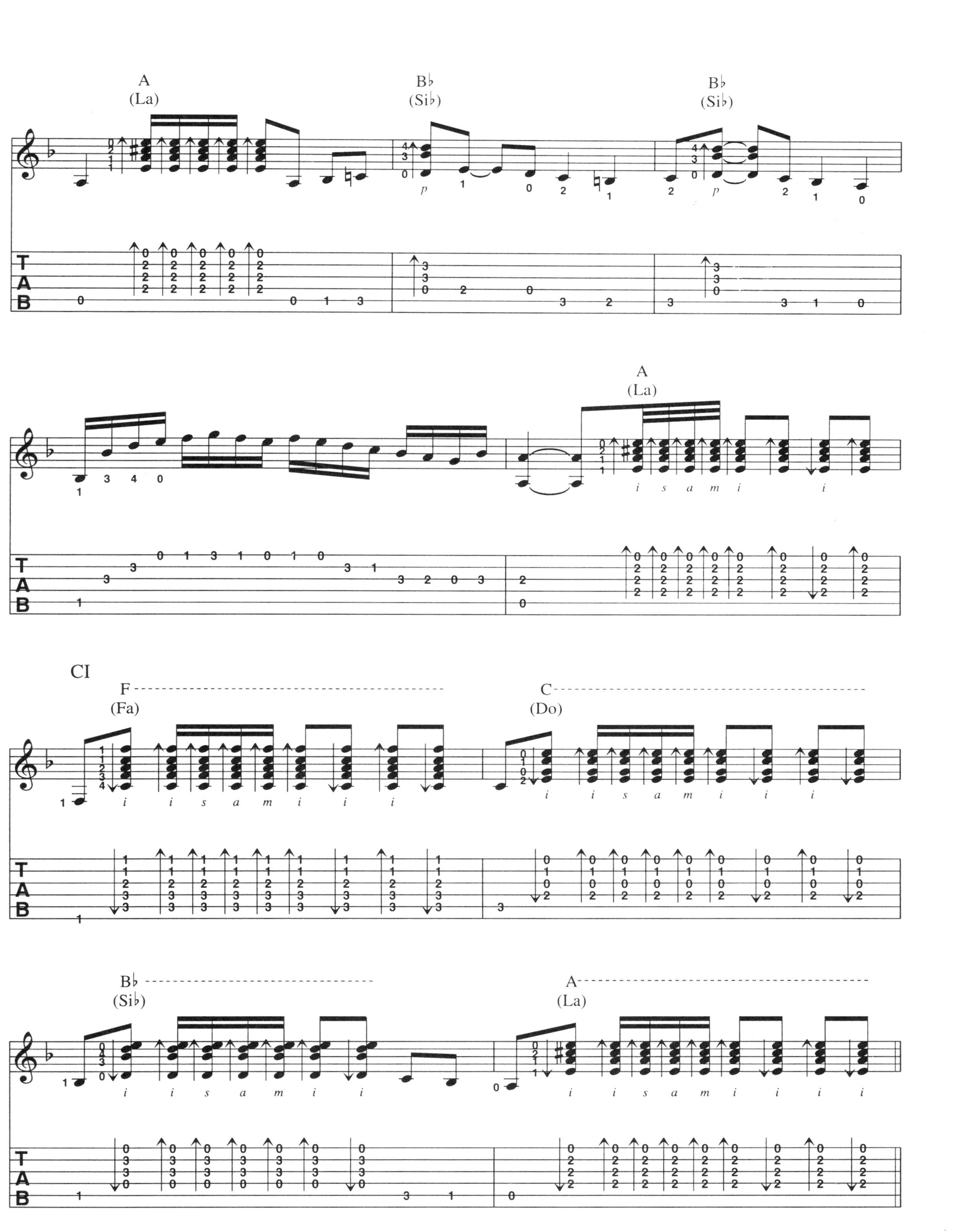
A
(La)
B♭
(Si♭)
B♭
(Si♭)
A
(La)
CI
F
(Fa)
C
(Do)
B♭
(Si♭)
A
(La)

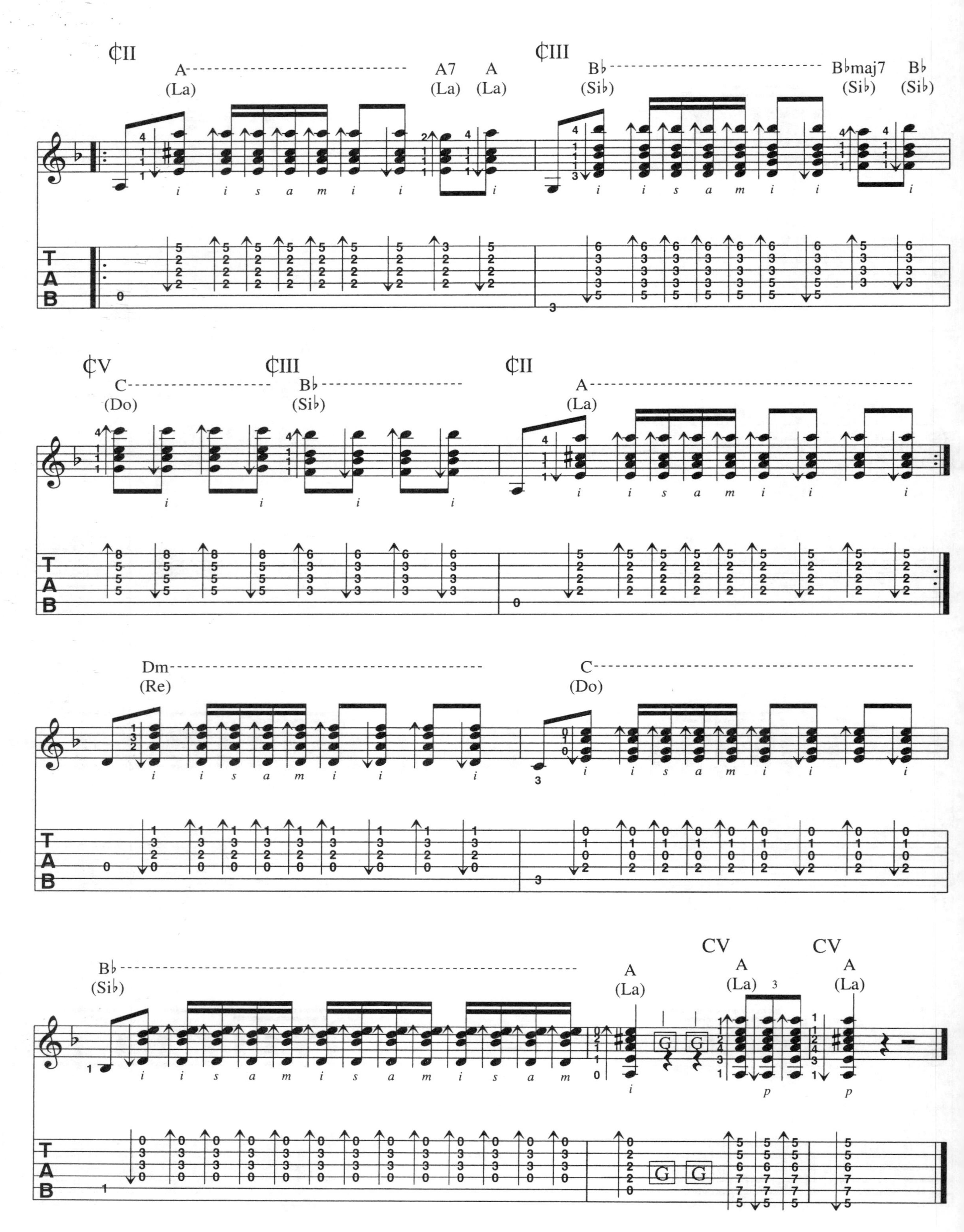
CII
A
(La)
A7
(La)
A
(La)
CIII
B♭
(Si♭)
B♭maj7
(Si♭)
B♭
(Si♭)
CV
C
(Do)
CIII
B♭
(Si♭)
CII
A
(La)
Dm
(Re)
C
(Do)
B♭
(Si♭)
A
(La)
CV
A
(La)
CV
A
(La)
G
G

Everybody's Music Teacher